uses of marijuana

uses of

marijuana

SOLOMON H. SNYDER, M.D.

Professor of Psychiatry and Pharmacology

THE JOHNS HOPKINS UNIVERSITY SCHOOL OF MEDICINE

New York
OXFORD UNIVERSITY PRESS
London   Toronto   1971

to Judith Rhea and Deborah Lynn
and their mom

acknowledgments

Material contained in the chapters Marijuana as Medicine and A Brief World History appeared as "What We Have Forgotten About Pot" in the *New York Times Magazine,* December 13, 1970, and is reprinted with the permission of the New York Times Co.

Material in the chapter Behavioral Effects was published in altered form in the May 1971 issue of *Psychology Today* and is reprinted with permission of CRM Publications.

A special note of gratitude is due to Nancy Brownley for her typing of the manuscript.

contents

uses of marijuana

marijuana as medicine

There was a time in the United States when extracts of cannabis were almost as commonly used for medicinal purposes as is aspirin today. Not only was cannabis a proprietary medication which could be purchased without a prescription in any drug store but it was also prescribed by physicians for the treatment of a broad variety of medical conditions, from migraines and excessive menstrual bleeding to ulcers, epilepsy, and even tooth decay.

Why is this wide medical use of the drug hardly known today? Were there legitimate medical reasons for its fall from respectability, or did legal restrictions largely account for the dramatic change? A look at the past usage of marijuana as medicine may help answer these questions, but first a few words about the nature of the drug are necessary.

Introduction

Cannabis, the generic name for marijuana, hashish, and related preparations, has been in use legally or illegally for about three hun-

3

Frank Leonardo.

dred years. Its source is the plant *Cannabis sativa,* also known as hemp. There are male and female forms, although, as may seem fitting for the mascot plant of the unisex generation, it has recently been cultivated in an hermaphroditic or single sexed variety. The psychoactive ingredients have, for roughly a thousand years, been assumed to derive almost exclusively from the female plant. Accordingly, great attention has traditionally been lavished on the cultivation of the female plant. Brazilian planters in the past would cut the terminal buds to induce more expanded branches, richer foliage and, consequently, more extractable marijuana. In Brazil traditions surrounding the plant were once so sexually charged that according to popular belief, this "castration" of the female plants had to be performed only by men! (1)

In the past year, however, direct chemical analyses of the pure psychotropic ingredient of the cannabis plant showed that it is present in equal concentration in male and female plants (2), a most embarrassing revelation for hemp growers in India, China, Europe, and the Americas, who have been discarding untold numbers of male plants.

Hemp grows freely as a weed in almost any climate, although the strains grown in warmer climates produce more of the resin that contains the psychoactive material. The exact chemical identity of this active ingredient was established in 1964 by an Israeli, Raphael Mechoulam, who showed it to be delta-l-tetrahydrocannabinol and was even able to synthesize it from simple basic chemicals (3). Delta-l-tetrahydrocannabinol, commonly referred to as THC, reproduces in man all the mind-altering effects that follow smoking or eating marijuana or hashish. In small doses THC produces a mild "high," while larger doses give rise to hallucinogenic and "psychotomimetic" (resembling psychosis) effects similar to a bad "trip" on LSD. Despite the similar subjective effects evoked by THC and LSD, THC bears no chemical resemblance to any psychedelic drug, not to LSD, mescaline, DMT, STP, psilocybin, or any others.

How do the many preparations of cannabis differ? Why are some frighteningly powerful and others pleasantly mild? This seems to depend on which part of the plant is used to manufacture the drug. The flowering leaves of ripe male and female hemp plants secrete a sticky resin which is the source of all, or almost all, of the THC in cannabis. Marijuana is a Mexican term—first applied to cheap tobacco and only in the late nineteenth century to cannabis—that refers to preparations in which leaves and stems of uncultivated plants are chopped up into something resembling crude tobacco leaf, with some seeds included. Accordingly, the THC content of marijuana is fairly low, and so its effects are moderate. In the United States, marijuana is usually smoked or baked into cookies. In India the same preparation is called "bhang" and is legal. It is blended conventionally into a liquid consumed at social gatherings, and is also prescribed by physicians for a variety of medical purposes.

In India the dried flowering tops of cultivated plants, covered with THC as a result of not having released their seeds, are used in preparing a somewhat more potent material called "ganja," which is usually smoked. Ganja is virtually unknown in the United States.

The most potent of all cannabis preparations is obtained by carefully scraping the THC-containing resin from the leaves of the cultivated plants. This gooey material is then pressed into hard blocks and smoked. In India it is known as charas and in other countries as hashish. The Indian pharmacologist, Chopra, has described another method of harvesting charas:

> Sometimes men dressed in leather suits or jackets pass through the fields of *Cannabis sativa* rubbing and crushing roughly against the plants early in the morning just after sunrise and when a fall of dew has taken place. The resinous material which sticks on is then scraped off their jackets and forms the charas resin of commerce. (4)

Hashish is about ten times as powerful as marijuana, and is the only cannabis derivative that has the capacity to produce hallucinogenic and psychotomimetic effects with any regularity.

In China, hemp was cultivated as a major source of fiber for the production of rope long before the Christian era began. There is little indication that its psychotropic properties were of much interest. Later, cannabis extracts were introduced in India, where they have continued for more than a thousand years to have medical applications. An Indian girl who worked for me as a laboratory technician told me the story of her experience with cannabis. She came from a wealthy family in Bombay and as a little girl was sent to one of the finest physicians in the city because her parents felt that she must put

Varieties of Cannabis

MILD FORMS	HOW PREPARED AND CONSUMED
MARIJUANA (European and American name)	The leaves and sometimes the stems and even seeds or entire plants are ground up and smoked or baked into cookies. The potency varies with THC content.
DAGGA (South Africa)	
KIF (North Africa)	
BHANG (Indian name, usually involves only leaves, is drunk and is usually somewhat richer in THC than American marijuana)	
INTERMEDIATE POTENCY	
GANJA (India)	Leaves close to the flowering tops of well-cultivated plants are harvested. Smoked, drunk, or baked into sweets. Not used outside India.
HIGH POTENCY	
CHARAS (India)	The resin which contains almost all the THC in the plant is scraped from the leaves near the flowering tops, pressed into blocks, and usually smoked.
HASHISH	

on weight if she was ever to attract a man. The doctor prescribed a glass of bhang before each meal, which enhanced her appetite. At seventeen she was a voluptuous, though not obese, young lady. She cannot recall any psychotropic effects, nor was she told by her physician to expect any.

The Nineteenth Century

Western medicine remained ignorant of cannabis until 1839 when W. B. O'Shaughnessy, a thirty-year-old Irish physician serving in India, published a forty-nine-page article on the drug in the Transactions of the Medical Society of Bengal (5). The ability to pinpoint historically the introduction of cannabis into European medicine is itself notable, since most drugs seem to slip gradually into medical use, usually having originated in folk medicine, with no identifiable discoverer or popularizer. O'Shaughnessy took upon himself the multiple roles of basic researcher, clinical pharmacologist, and practitioner, a rare combination today. He reviewed the literature on the use of cannabis in Indian medicine during the preceding nine hundred years. A cautious man, he was not satisfied with the extensive record of safety and conducted a series of animal experiments to characterize its effects as well as the limits of dosage. He found cannabis to be remarkably safe in animals, a property which has been rediscovered many times. In fact, despite many escalations of dose he could not kill any mice, rats, or rabbits. It is now well known that cannabis is one of the least lethal of all drugs. O'Shaughnessy then administered the drug to patients suffering from seizures, rheumatism, tetanus, and rabies. His most clear-cut findings were that cannabis relieved pain and acted as a muscle relaxant and an anticonvulsant.

O'Shaughnessy's findings excited the interest of clinicians throughout Europe and there soon appeared in nineteenth-century medical journals descriptions of its application in a large number of diverse conditions, including menstrual cramps, asthma, childbirth psychosis, quinsy, cough, insomnia, migraine headaches, withdrawal from opiates, and chorea. One investigator summarized its applications as follows:

> It acts as a soporific or hypnotic causing sleep; as an anodyne in lulling irritation; as an antispasmodic in checking cough and cramp; as a nervine stimulant in removing languor and anxiety; also in raising the pulse and enlivening the spirits, without any drawback or deduction of indirect or incidental convenience; conciliating tranquil repose without causing nausea, constipation or other signs of effect or indigestion, without headache or stupor (6).

One must be cautious in accepting such glowing endorsements uncritically since "languor and anxiety" are readily relieved by the power of suggestion and a sugar pill. But positive testimonials on the part of the medical profession were by no means isolated. In his standard textbook, *A System of Practical Therapeutics,* Hobart Hare, a professor of medicine at the Jefferson Medical College in Philadelphia, gave the following account:

> Cannabis is very valuable for the relief of pain, particularly that depending on nerve disturbances; it produces sleep; it gives great relief in paralysis and tends to quiet tremors . . . and it is used in spasm of the bladder due to cystitis or nervousness; it is used in cough mixtures and does not constipate or depress the system as does morphine. (7)

Wood's *Treatise on Therapeutics* stated that: "*Cannabis indica* is used chiefly for the relief of pain; especially of neuralgic character, although it will palliate even pain of organic origin. It is also of service for quieting conditions of restlessness and general discomfort—for instance in neurasthenia—and to relieve the distress of the later stages of incurable diseases, especially advanced phthisis. . . . It is used as a mild somnificiant." (8)

In the nineteenth century the most abundant source of cannabis for medical use was extracts of the hemp plant imported from India. Since India was then a colony of England, British physicians were responsible for the first explorations of the medical applications of this drug. Of course, this was long before the current era of superspecialization in medicine, so that individual doctors researched and treated patients with a wide variety of diagnoses. One of these Renaissance men of medicine, J. Russell Reynolds, a physician to Queen Victoria, made a careful evaluation of cannabis in many conditions over a thirty-year period. He was particularly impressed with its ability to relieve pain: "In almost all painful maladies I have found Indian hemp by far the most useful of drugs; and it is especially so in those cases which are to the present time relegated ot the 'functional' order." (9) His observation that the drug was particularly effective in functional pain, that is, where an emotional or psychosomatic element aggravated the pain, is of special interest. Perhaps it was because cannabis released neurotic inhibitions and had a mild sedative and euphoric effect that it could so remarkably ease "nervous" pain. In much the same way today a mild barbituate combined with aspirin and caffeine, called Fiorinal, constitutes the most effective remedy for tension-headache in modern medicine. Reynolds especially recommended cannabis for migraine headaches: "Very many victims of the malady [migraine] have for years kept their sufferings in abeyance by taking hemp at the moment of threatening or onset of the attack." In a similar vein, the prestigious British journal *The Lancet,* in one of its periodic reviews of valuable therapies, reported: "Indian hemp, night and morning and continued for sometime, is the most valuable remedy met with in the treatment of persistent headache." (10)

Migraine headaches can be so incapacitating that, besides easing the acute pain, it is important to attempt to prevent future attacks or at least reduce their frequency and severity. In modern medicine these two tasks are the province of two different types of drugs. Ergot derivatives, such as ergotamine, alleviate acute migraine headaches, while methysergide (Sansert)—which, interestingly, is a close relative of LSD—is used to ward off future headaches. There are indications that cannabis may fulfill both roles. Thus Hobart Hare concluded that "Hemp is by far the most active agent in subduing the pain [of migraine headaches] and in preventing other attacks. . . . I have certainly seen very severe and intractable cases of migraine successfully treated by this remedy, not only in regard to the attack itself but *by acting as a prophylactic.*" (11) Hare also found evidence that the tranquilizing effects of cannabis may contribute to its value:

> During the time that this remarkable drug is relieving pain a very curious psychical condition sometimes manifests itself; namely, that the diminution of the pain seems to be due to its fading away in the distance so that the pain becomes less and less, just as the pain in a delicate ear would grow less and less as a beaten drum was carried further and further out of the range of hearing. This condition is probably associated with other well known symptoms produced by the drug, namely, the prolongation of time.

One type of pain that might be alleviated by a drug that especially relieves "nervous" pain is that of menstrual cramps, since its relative severity is likely to be determined by emotional factors. Indeed, cannabis was used extensively for menstrual cramps in the nineteenth century, and physicians soon discovered that it also relieved excessive menstrual bleeding or menorrhagia. Its successes here were reported to have been spectacular. For instance, John Brown reported in *The British Medical Journal*: "Indian hemp has such specific use in menorrhagia—there is no medicine which has given such good results; for this reason it ought to take the first place as a remedy in menorrhagia . . . the failures are so few that I venture to call it a specific in menorrhagia." (12) Even more strikingly, Robert Batho in the same journal claimed that "It [cannabis] is *par excellance* the remedy for that condition [menorrhagia] . . . it is so certain in its power of controlling menorrhagia that it is a valuable aid to diagnosis in cases where it is uncertain whether an early abortion may or may not have occurred." (13) To be able to use the favorable response to a drug as a diagnosis—as the restoration to alertness of a comatose patient by an intravenous injection of glucose diagnoses insulin coma—the drug must be extremely reliable in its action. How cannabis could slow down menstrual hemorrhage with such reliability is something of a mystery.

Like the present-day narcotic pain relievers such as codeine, cannabis was used frequently to control coughs. While today this may not seem to be an important area of therapeutics, in the nineteenth century when tuberculosis was the leading killer of young men and women and caused a great deal of debilitation simply by evoking incessant, intractable coughing, any medicine that could ease the cough was a blessing.

Since cannabis was introduced at a time when opiates were prescribed freely, and resultant addiction was far more widespread than it is today, it was natural that cannabis should be tested as an adjunct in withdrawing patients from opium and other addicting drugs, including alcohol and chloral hydrate. For instance, Edward Birch reported in *The Lancet*:

> I am satisfied of its immense value [in withdrawing patients from chloral hydrate or opium] . . . the chief point that struck me was the immediate action of the drug in appeasing the appetite for the chloral or opium and restoring the ability to appreciate food. . . . I prescribed the cannabis simply with a view to utilizing a well known remedy for insomnia, but it did much more than procure sleep. (14)

The potential value of cannabis in helping to withdraw patients from alcohol or opium was rediscovered about fifty years later during the extensive investigation of the marijuana problem in New York City sponsored by Mayor Fiorella LaGuardia. It was found that by substituting cannabis for heroin "The withdrawal symptoms were ameliorated or eliminated sooner, the patient was in a better frame of mind, his spirits were elevated, his physical condition was more rapidly rehabilitated, and he expressed the wish to resume his occupation sooner." (15) When Roger Adams isolated and synthesized some active tetrahydrocannabinol components of cannabis (16), they were also tried out in alcoholism and heroin addiction with equivocal results (17).

Why might cannabis be helpful in easing withdrawal from narcotics and alcohol? Its utility is probably related, in part, to some of its actions as an anti-anxiety, tranquilizer-like drug. Anti-anxiety agents such as chlordiazepoxide (Librium) and paraldehyde are also effective in treating alcohol withdrawal, especially the *delirium tremens*. Going back over the reports of cannabis use in narcotics and alcohol withdrawal, one is struck with the suggestion by investigators that, besides easing the craving for the addictive agent, cannabis seemed to have a general tonic effect, improving the physical state of the addict, and elevating his spirits, increasing his appetite.

In O'Shaughnessy's first report of the uses of cannabis in medicine, he cited its value in controlling convulsions. At that time convulsions resulting from many different disorders were lumped together, whereas today epilepsy can be distinguished from other causes of convulsions. There followed reports of the use of cannabis in treating chorea resulting from rheumatic fever, in which wild flailing of the arms, St. Vitus's dance, resembled convulsions (18). However, its possible value in epilepsy remained untested until routine screening of many chemicals for anticonvulsant activity in animals suggested that the congener of tetrahydrocannabinol, the "active" ingredient of cannabis synthesized by Adams, might have anticonvulsant properties (19). Whereupon Davis and Ramsey proceeded to test some tetrahydrocannabinol analogues in epileptic children (20). At this time, the late 1940's, the convulsive attacks of most epileptics could be controlled by diphenylhydantoin (Dilantin) or phenobarbital, still the major anti-epileptic drugs in medical practice. Not wanting to try a questionable new agent on children who might be helped by traditional drugs, Davis and Ramsey chose five institutionalized epileptic children whose attacks could not be controlled with phenobarbital, Dilantin, or even a combination of the two. By contrast, with tetrahydrocannabinol, two of the five became almost completely seizure-free, and the other three did at least as well as they had on their previous medical regimen.

It is striking that so many of these medical reports fail to mention any intoxicating properties of the drug. Rarely, if ever, is there any indication that patients—hundreds of thousands must have received cannabis in Europe in the nineteenth century—were "stoned" or changed their attitudes toward work, love, their fellow men, or their homeland. It is unlikely that the cannabis plants grown fifty to eighty years ago differed in chemical composition from those growing today. More likely, the difference is a matter of the patient's expectations. When people see their doctor about a specific malady, they expect a specific treatment and do not anticipate being "turned on." And recent investigations have indicated that the mental effects of cannabis are tremendously dependent on the expectation of the subject. When speaking of the patient's expectations, one is reminded of the placebo effect, that positive therapeutic results may derive from the doctor's suggestion and not the drug. This is particularly likely to take place with "nervous pain." Accordingly, the enthusiastic reports of marijuana as medication should be interpreted with caution until the results are confirmed by modern "placebo-proof" research.

Since the major use of cannabis in the nineteenth century was as a pain killer or mild tranquilizer, and since opium was then the most widely used drug for these purposes, it is natural that many medical reports on cannabis focused on a comparison of the virtues and drawbacks of these two drugs. One of the most obviously valuable features of cannabis, apparently quite clear to nineteenth-century physicians, although not yet crystal clear in the eyes of the United States Narcotics Bureau, was that the prolonged use of cannabis did not result in the development of tolerance (increase in resistance to a drug's effects so that the dose must be raised to produce the original effects), nor did it lead to physical dependence. This was commented on again and again in nineteenth-century medical journals, was reconfirmed in the sociological as well as medical investigations of Mayor La-Guardia's committee on the marijuana problem in New York, and has once again been reconfirmed in studies during the last three years using both crude cannabis and THC.

In addition, cannabis products are far less toxic than the opiates.

The latter, including morphine and heroin, can kill by depressing the respiratory centers in the brain, and do so in amounts only a few times greater than therapeutic doses. In contrast, the minimal toxicity of cannabis was demonstrated by O'Shaughnessy, and his results have been repeated over and over again.

What about effects on the vegetative functions of the body? Opiates slow down the churning of the intestines and routinely produce constipation. Since opiate alkaloids retard bile and pancreatic secretions, the digestion of food is slowed. Opiates retard the flow of bile by constricting the bile ducts so that the pressure inside them builds up, sometimes causing severe colic pain. Another unpleasant side effect of opiates is their tendency to cause nausea and vomiting. Cannabis produces none of these effects.

In one important way opiates are better than cannabis. They are stronger pain-killers. For the excruciating colicky pain produced by a kidney stone or the crushing chest pain of an acute heart attack, morphine is a blessing. For these conditions cannabis is much too weak. But its relatively weak pain-relieving action could not possibly account for the neglect of cannabis in modern medicine. For there are many conditions, such as migraine headaches or menstrual cramps, where something as mild as aspirin gives insufficient relief and opiates are too powerful, not to mention their potential for addiction. Cannabis might conceivably fulfill a useful role in such conditions.

Decline and Fall

Returning to our original questions, why has cannabis been so neglected in recent years? Although legal restrictions are at fault to a large extent, they cannot be the sole reason. Well before the Marijuana Stamp Act of 1937, in the late nineteenth and early twentieth century, the use of cannabis in general medicine was already declining.

There had always been problems in prescribing this drug. It is insoluble in water and so cannot be injected intravenously for rapid effect. Moreover, the delay before it begins to take effect when given by mouth, one to two hours, is longer than with many other drugs.

Even more troublesome was the difficulty in obtaining standard batches of cannabis during the nineteenth century. Different batches would vary widely in their potency, probably because the amount of resin in plants varies with degree of ripeness, humidity, soil characteristics, temperature, and time of year. In the early days of cannabis usage in European medicine, the drug became very controversial in this respect. On the one hand, highly reputed physicians were praising it as a "miracle drug." At the same time others became incensed at their failure to reproduce the therapeutic successes of their colleagues, going along with Oliver's conclusion that cannabis "is hardly worthy of a place on our list of remedial agents." (21) It is likely that the "therapeutic failures" simply reflected weak or inactive preparations. This variability was well known even to O'Shaughnessy, who observed considerable deterioration during transport of the drug from India to England, "for he had frequently obtained marked effects abroad, from half a grain of extract . . . and considered one grain and a half a large dose. In this country he had given as much as ten or twelve grains before the desired effect was produced." Reynolds, whose extensive experience with cannabis has been mentioned already, was also familiar with this lack of uniformity: "the drug is one, which, by its nature and the forms of its administration, is liable to great variations in strength . . . and extracts cannot be made uniform, because the hemp grown during different seasons and in different places, varies in the amount that it contains of the therapeutic agent."

Reynolds, an astute and wise clinician, also discerned another difficulty, the variability among individuals in their response to the same dose of cannabis: "individuals differ widely in their relations to many medicines and articles of diet especially those of vegetable origin—such as tea, coffee, ipecac, digitalis . . . and *cannabis.*"

In the mid-nineteenth century, however, none of these difficulties seemed insuperable. Variations in individual response and in the potency of different batches of the drug could be readily taken into account by starting patients with a small dose which might then be increased gradually. The one- or two-hour delay before the drug took effect could be tolerated since most of the conditions to be treated by cannabis were not life-threatening emergencies. For the same reason, it did not seem too troublesome that cannabis could not be dissolved in water and injected intravenously.

It was probably the introduction of a variety of new synthetic drugs that started the decline of cannabis. A major factor was the introduction of the hypodermic syringe into American medicine from England. This facilitated the use of fast-acting, water-soluble opiate drugs, a practice which rapidly proliferated as numerous casualties in the Civil War were treated with intravenous morphine. Although the danger of opiate addiction had been well known since antiquity, somehow physicians managed to ignore it when they were presented with the convenient tool of injectable morphine. Opiate addiction was so prevalent among soldiers who had received it for their wounds that it came to be called the "soldier's disease" after the Civil War.

A few cautious physicians warned against what were soon to be the tragic results of this reckless use of morphine. Mattison in 1891 reminded his colleagues of these difficulties and recommended cannabis instead: "With a wish for speedy effect, it is so easy to use that modern mischief-maker, hypodermic morphia, that they [young physicians] are prone to forget remote results of incautious opiate-giving. Would that the wisdom which has come to their professional fathers . . . might serve them to steer clear of narcotic shoals on which many a patient has gone awreck." By contrast, he felt that "My experience warrants this statement: cannabis indica is a safe and successful anodyne and hypnotic." (22)

In addition to the increasing use of morphine, the new synthetic analgesics such as aspirin and the new tranquilizers and sleeping pills such as barbiturates and chloral hydrate tended to replace cannabis. Of course, like morphine, while these new drugs were more efficient than cannabis, they had their drawbacks. Aspirin seems to be a less potent pain-killer than cannabis, and it lacks the relaxing sedative actions of cannabis. Barbiturates, of course, are prone to addictive abuse. Even worse, the lethal dose of barbiturates is so treacherously close to the therapeutic dose that these drugs are the most frequently employed chemical means for committing suicide. And those who use them indiscriminately for night-time sedation, even if they are not barbiturate addicts, occasionally are dead the next morning from accidental overdoses or synergistic actions of barbiturates and alcoholic beverages. In fact, it is quite edifying to compare, as did Dr. T. Mikuriya (23), the ratio of lethal and effective doses for secobarbital (commercially marketed as Seconal), alcohol, and pure THC. This ratio, called the "safety factor" of drugs, is about 10 for Seconal and alcohol and about 40,000 for THC.

To summarize, cannabis fell from favor in medical practice for several reasons. The major one was the variable potency of different batches of the drug, due to variation in the THC content among different plants. Other reasons were its lack of solubility, so that it could not be injected, and its delay in acting after ingestion, also, the increased use of morphine, aspirin, and barbiturates played a role. The case was closed when cannabis became practically inaccessible as a result of the 1937 Marijuana Stamp Act.

But some of these objections to the employment of cannabis extracts in medicine may soon be resolved by new research. Since the isolation and synthesis of delta-l-tetrahydrocannabinol in 1964, this pure active ingredient has been shown to reproduce most of the known effects of cannabis quite reliably. Thus it can be given in pure form and in known dosage with predictable effects.

What is even more interesting is the possibility of developing variations of the THC molecule which may retain selectively certain of the actions of cannabis. This is not merely speculation. Quite recently Sim tried out several variants of the THC molecule in human subjects. (24). One of these had very marked blood pressure lowering effects at doses which produced few, if any, mental changes. Sim suggested that this drug might be valuable for the hypertensive patient. O'Shaughnessy's original report suggested the use of cannabis for what was probably high blood pressure. Currently several major American drug companies are working feverishly, synthesizing new analogues of the THC with the expressed aim of developing agents useful in clinical medicine for a variety of maladies. This activity, of course, goes on despite the official status of cannabis as a "dangerous drug."

References

1. Doria, R.: Proc. 2nd Pan-American Sci. Congress, 9:151, 1916.
2. Valle, J. R., Lapa, A. J., and Barros, G. G.: J. Pharm. Pharmacol., 20:798, 1968.
3. Gaoni, Y., and Mechoulam, R.: J. Amer. Chem. Soc., 86:1646, 1964.

4. Chopra, R. N.: *Indigenous Drugs of India*, The Art Press, Calcutta, 1933, p. 78.
5. O'Shaughnessy, W. B.: Trans, Med. Phys. Soc., Bengal, 1838-1840, p. 71.
6. Aulde, J.: Ther. Gazette, 6:523, 1890.
7. Hare, H. A., and Chrystie, W.: *A System of Practical Therapeutics*, Lee Brothers, Philadelphia, 1892, vol. 3.
8. Wood, H. C. J.: *Treatise on Therapeutics*, 6th edition, J. B. Lippincott and Company, Philadelphia, 1886.
9. Reynolds, J. R.: The Lancet, March 22, 1890, p. 637.
10. Letter from London: The Lancet, December 3, 1887, p. 732.
11. Hare, H. A.: Ther. Gazette, 11:225, 1887.
12. Brown, J.: Brit. Med. J., May 26, 1883, p. 1002.
13. Batho, R.: Brit. Med. J., 1:1004, 1883.
14. Birch, E. A.: The Lancet, March 30, 1889, p. 625.
15. Allentuck, S., and Bowman, K.: Amer. J. Psych., 99:248, 1942.
16. Adams, R.: Bull. N. Y. Acad. Sci., 18:705, 1942.
17. Thompson, L., and Proctor, R. C.: North Carolina Med. J., 14:520, 1953.
18. Douglass, J.: Edinburgh Med. J., 14:777, 1896.
19. Loewe, S., and Goodman, L. S.: Fed. Proc., 6:352, 1947.
20. Davis, J. P., and Ramsey, H.: Fed. Proc., 8:285, 1949.
21. Oliver, J.: Brit. Med. J., 1:905, 1883.
22. Mattison, J. B.: St. Louis Med. Surg. J., 61:265, 1891.
23. Mikuriya, T.: New Physician, November 1969, p. 902.
24. Sim, V.: in *Psychotomimetic Drugs*, edited by Efron D. H. Raven Press, New York, 1970, p. 332.

 *a brief world history*

Origins in India and China

The pain-killing powers of cannabis were known thousands of years ago to the Chinese physician Hoa-Gho (1), who mixed the resin with wine. This preparation, called *ma-yo,* was employed as an anesthetic for controlling pain during surgical operations. Besides alleviating pain, it seems to have had the ability to cause amnesia for the operation, much like the "twilight sleep" produced by scopolamine, a drug used to prevent secretions during operations and as a sedative. There seems to be very little evidence of the use of this drug for its psycho-active properties, though some early Chinese writings refer to cannabis as the "liberator of sin." Probably there was a certain amount of controversy over the merits of cannabis in ancient China as there is today in the United States, since other Chinese writers refer to cannabis as the "delight giver."

As a mind-altering substance, cannabis seems to have come of age in India, where the Hindu used cannabis as an aid in meditation. Its religious role is suggested by the following quotation from native literature:

19

> To the Hindu the hemp plant is holy. A guardian lives in
> bhang . . . Bhang is the joy giver, the sky flier, the heav-
> enly guide, the poor man's heaven, the soother of grief . . .
> No god or man is as good as the religious drinker of bhang.
> The students of the scriptures of Benares are given bhang
> before they sit to study. At Benares, Ujjain and other holy
> places, yogis take deep draughts of bhang that they may
> center their thoughts on the Eternal . . . By the help of
> bhang ascetics pass days without food or drink. The support-
> ing power of bhang has brought many a Hindu family safe
> through the miseries of famine. (2)

Even in India there was apparently some angry discussion about
the possible value or danger of cannabis, as is implied in the following warning from the same native writer:

> To forbid or even seriously to restrict the use of so holy and
> gracious a herb as the hemp would cause widespread suffer-
> ing and annoyance and to large bands of worshipped ascetics
> deep seeded anger. It would rob the people of a solace in dis-
> comfort, of a cure in sickness, of a guardian whose gracious
> protection saves them for the attacks of evil influences . . .
> so grand a result, so tiny a sin!

Disapproval of cannabis may have originated with the Christian
missionaries and other Europeans. In a study of Hindu mystics, J.
Campbell Oman noted that Christian missionaries often remarked
that a "great number of Hindu saints live in a state of perpetual intoxication and call this stupefaction, which arises from smoking
intoxicating herbs, fixing the mind on god" (3).

Since India plays such an important role in the history of cannabis
and since patterns of the drug's use do not seem to have changed
much there in the past thousand years, it may be worthwhile to digress
from history to examine cultural factors relevant to current cannabis use in India. George Morris Carstairs (4), professor of psychiatry at the University of Edinburgh and a world authority on trans-
cultural psychiatry, lived in a village in Northern India in 1951
where he was struck by one unexpected aspect of the caste system
which permeates Hindu society. The community had some paradoxi-
cal attitudes toward the two most prevalent intoxicants, daru, a potent alcoholic beverage distilled from the flowers of the mahwa tree,

and bhang. The warrior caste, the Rajputs, used daru exclusively, and seemed to regard cannabis as an indulgence fit only for sissies. The Brahmins, on the other hand, employed cannabis in both religious and social settings. Rajputs, of course, represent the temporal aristocracy as Brahmins do the spiritual. Until the social reforms of 1948, the rajahs of the Rajput class exercised arbitrary and autocratic rule over innumerable small principalities. In their upbringing, great stress is placed on individual bravery in the face of danger, and although the test of real danger seldom arises nowadays, the young Rajput still lives with the anxiety that some day he may not prove adequate to the occasion. As a result, the Rajputs in the village where Carstairs lived tended to be boastful, touchy, and readily inclined to assuage their anxieties in the convivial relaxation of a drinking party. In their drinking bouts they were "taking a holiday from sober concerns." Although nominally they prided themselves on drinking with discrimination, a fixed measure for each day, their restraint often vanished in the course of an evening's drinking.

The Brahmins in the village unequivocally denounced the use of daru. They felt it was inimical to their religious life whose first requirement was to "abhor meat and wine." Interestingly, Carstairs found that the gentle Brahmin priests were far more vitriolic in reviling daru than were the Rajputs in their disinterested disdain for cannabis. The ruler of the village, a Rajput, thought himself to be a religious man and often tried to reconcile his religious devotion with his indulgence in alcohol. This was vehemently rejected by the Brahmins, one of whom said, "He is all wrong; he is a bogus lecher always busy with wine and women, how can he find his way along this stony and thorny path?"

Brahmins in the village would often visit a nearby pilgrimage center. The chief object of worship there was a large black stone phallic symbol, one representation of the god Shiva. The god was often cited as a bhang drinker. The Brahmins would attempt to model themselves on Shiva, and the more ascetic among them would practice prolonged austerities, attempting to withdraw their attention entirely from distractions of the sensible world until they could exist for hours in oblivious introspection, the ultimate reward being to divest oneself of one's body. Bhang was the *sine qua non* in achieving this state of detachment, and in his visits to the temple Carstairs would generally encounter large numbers of holy men staggering about "stoned out of their minds."

Carstairs was struck by the similarity among Western Europeans, Americans, and the Rajputs in their commitment to a life of action. All share an upbringing which values individual achievement highly and considers sensual indulgence to be not wholly wrong if enjoyed within socially prescribed limits. The Brahmin theme of surrendering one's powers of volition is unfamiliar, distasteful, and threatening to most Westerners, excluding young drug-users. Carstairs admitted:

> "The present writer would have to say that of the two types of intoxication which he witnessed and in a measure shared, he had no doubt that that which was indulged in by the Brahmins was the less socially disruptive, less unseemly, and more in harmony with the highest ideas of their race; and yet so alien to his own personal and cultural pattern of ego defences that he much preferred the other."

In the earlier Christian era, cannabis was known for its mind-altering properties largely in India. After A.D. 1000 its use began spreading westward, and references in the Persian and other Arabian literature began to appear.

The Near East: Hashish and the Assassins

One of the most fascinating stories about the use of cannabis in Muslim cultures was told by Marco Polo. It dealt with the religious leader, Hasan-Ibn-Sabbah, who lived in the 11th century A.D. and over the years has come to be known as the "Old Man of the Mountain." Hasan came from a prominent family in Arabia and was well educated in Egypt. Although he began his professional life as a religious missionary, Hasan soon developed a surprisingly modern agnostic philosophy and gathered together a secret cult of followers. He trained his followers as an army and succeeded in capturing a number of fortresses, using religion and philosophy as political or military tools. He is best known for refining the practice of assassination to an art—and herein lies the relevance of this tale to cannabis, as well as an interesting problem for philologists.

The assassins were specially recruited young men in their late teens and early twenties. They were all well treated, well paid, and

sworn to total allegiance to Hasan. Marco Polo described a remarkable garden that Hasan constructed at his major fortress, the Alamut,
where the young assassins were entertained under intriguing circumstances. They would be transported there only after imbibing enough
hashish to put them to sleep, and upon waking would be over-
whelmed with the unearthly splendor of the garden:

> He [Hasan] kept at his Court a number of the youths of the
> country, from twelve to twenty years of age, such as had a
> taste for soldiering . . . Then he would introduce them to
> his Garden, some four, or six, or ten at a time, having first
> made them drink a certain potion [hashish] which cast them
> into a deep sleep, and then causing them to be lifted and
> carried in. So when they awoke they found themselves in
> the Garden. . .
> When therefore they awoke, and found themselves in a
> place so charming, they deemed that it was Paradise in very
> truth. And the ladies and damsels dallied with them to their
> hearts' content. . .
> So when the Old Man would have any prince slain, he
> would say to such a youth: Go thou and slay So and So; and
> when thou returneth my Angels shall bear thee into Paradise.
> And shouldst thou die, natheless even so will I send my
> Angels to carry thee back into Paradise.(5)

Although this tale may well be apocryphal, most philologists seem
to agree that the concept of assassination derives from Hasan-Ibn-
Sabbah. There is, however, dispute among them as to whether the
word *assassin* comes from *Hasan* or *hashish*. Some maintain that
hashish itself derives from *Hasan*.

Cannabis must have been quite popular in the Arab world during
the Middle Ages. In the "Thousand and One Nights," also known
as "The Tales of Scheherazade," a collection of folk talkes made between roughly A.D. 1000 and 1700, there are many references to
bhang, called "beng" by the Arabians, as well as to hashish. For instance, one chapter gives the following description of the preparation and consumption of hashish:

> Furthermore I conceive that the twain are eaters of Hash-
> ish, which drug when swallowed by man, maketh him prat-
> tle of whatso he pleaseth and chooseth, making him now a

Sultan, then a Wazir, and then a merchant, the while it seemeth to him that the world is in the hollow of his hand. Tis composed of hemp leaflets whereto are added aromatic roots and somewhat of sugar; then they cook it and prepare a kind of confection which they eat, but whoso eateth it (especially if he eat more than enough) talketh of matters which reason may on no wise represent. (6)

In Europe

Cannabis was probably brought to Europe by Napoleon's soldiers returning from Egypt. At least it is well documented that in Egypt Napoleon discovered a widespread use of hashish, particularly among the lower classes. He even issued a proclamation prohibiting its sale or use.

Between 1840 and 1860 in Paris, a distinguished group of writers became fascinated by the hashish experience. The group included Théophile Gautier, Charles Baudelaire, and Alexandre Dumas. Their written descriptions probably still constitute the clearest, most thorough accounts of the effects of cannabis on the psyche.

How did this "literary epoch" in the history of cannabis come about? Jacques Moreau de Tours was a prominent French psychiatrist at the Hospital of the Bicêtre who became interested in treating his patients with cannabis. He introduced the drug to the author, Théophile Gautier, then twenty-four years old. Gautier was intrigued with the effects of the drug and founded the famous "Le Club des Hachichins" at the Hotel Pimodan on the Isle Saint-Louis, close to the Latin Quarter of Paris. There they ate a sweet meat, Dawamesc, which had been introduced to the romantic society of the day from Algeria as a dessert delicacy. It contained large quantities of hashish, and the literary records of the Club's members, accordingly, reflect high dose effects of cannabis. Gautier was the first to publish his account of the drug, in 1843, in a book entitled *Club des Hachichins* (7):

> After several minutes a sense of numbness overwhelmed me. It seemed that my body had dissolved and become transparent. I saw very clearly inside me the Hashish I had eaten, in the form of an emerald which radiated millions of tiny

sparks. The lashes of my eyes elongated themselves to Infinity, rolling like threads of gold on little ivory wheels, which spun about with an amazing rapidity. All around me I heard the shattering and crumbling of jewels of all colors, songs renewed themselves without ceasing, as in the play of a kaleidoscope. At certain moments, I still saw my comrades, but disfigured and grotesque, half men, half plants. The spectacle was so ridiculous that I writhed with laughter in my corner and, in order to take part in this buffoonery, I hurled my cushions in the air catching them and throwing them again with the rapidity of an Indian juggler . . . One of the gentlemen addressed to me a discourse in Italian which the Hashish, by its omnipotence, transposed to me in Spanish.

On an LSD trip, to feel that languages are being transposed usually demands a whopping dose. Hashish would rarely produce such an effect and marijuana, almost never. Probably Gautier was exquisitely sensitive to the drug's effects because of his extravagant expectations and the eerie, elaborate accoutrements of the meeting room of the Club. Besides, Gautier was a writer given to hyperbole, not likely to underplay his story. He goes on:

The first stage drew to an end. After several minutes I found myself with all my composure, without a headache and without any of the symptoms which accompany the intoxication of wine, and altogether quite astonished at the things which had happened. A half-hour had scarcely passed when I fell again under the power of the Hashish. This time the vision was much more complicated and extraordinary. Thousands of millions of butterflies, with wings rustling like fans, perpetually swarmed in an atmosphere which was faintly luminous. . . . My hearing was prodigiously developed; I heard the sound of colors; green, red, blue, and yellow sounds came to me in distinct waves. An over-turned glass, a low-spoken word, vibrated and echoed through me like the reverberations of thunder. My own voice seemed so powerful that I dared not speak for fear of breaking the walls and making myself burst like a bomb . . . I was absorbed in a vast emptiness and became wholly disengaged from myself, entirely absent from my body, that odious witness which accompanies you always. . . . There was something particular in the intoxication of Hashish, that is, it is not continuous, it

takes you and it leaves you, you mount to Heaven and you
fall back to Earth without transition—as in insanity there are
lucid moments.

Despite some exaggeration, it is unlikely that Gautier fabricated this
passage, for it is as precise and rigorous a dissection of many aspects
of the subjective effects of psychedelic agents as the most painstaking
modern psychologists have been able to provide. Gautier elegantly
verbalizes the phenomenon of "synesthesia," in which sensory modali-
ties are interchanged. Synesthesia occurs most frequently with psychedelic drugs like LSD, but also may accompany high doses of cannabis.
Gautier also alludes to the wave-like effect in which a lucid in-
terval can divide the drug experience into discrete entities. He de-
scribes a feeling of disembodiment, merging of the self with the total
universe, which probably is the major *raison d'être* for the hallowed
place of cannabis in Hindu mysticism.

Alexandre Dumas was impressed that hashish enhances erotic sensations. He wrote about this in the *Count of Monte Cristo* and thus
anticipated Timothy Leary by a hundred years in wrongly pro-
nouncing cannabis to be an aphrodisiac (8):

> And then followed a dream of passion like that promised
> by the Prophet to the Elect. Lips of stone turned to flame,
> breasts of ice became like heated lava, so that to Franz, yield-
> ing for the first time to the sway of the drug, love was a
> sorrow and voluptuousness a torture, as burning mouths were
> pressed to his thirsty lips, and he was held in cool serpent-
> like embraces.

Charles Baudelaire dealt with his hashish experiences in a book
entitled *The Artificial Paradise* (9). Like Gautier, he was entranced
by the sensory effects of the drug, which he described with precision,
again referring to synthesia. Baudelaire even maintained that he experienced hallucinations, in the sense of seeing things for which
there is no concrete evidence at all, an effect hardly ever produced
by cannabis or even LSD. Baudelaire felt that:

> The senses become extraordinarily acute and fine. The
> eyes pierce Infinity. The ear perceives the most imperceptible
> in the midst of the sharpest noises. Hallucinations begin. Ex-

ternal objects take on monstrous appearances and reveal themselves under forms hitherto unknown. . . . The most singu-
lar equivocations, the most inexplicable transposition of ideas
takes place. Sounds have odor and colors are musical.

Although the experience of the 1960's in the United States suggests that the use or abuse of cannabis tends to spread like plague,
the chronicle of the past two millennia throughout the world bespeaks
a slower rate. Until about A.D. 1000, cannabis was employed for psychotropic purposes in India and to a much lesser extent in China. In the
next five hundred years or so, its use reached the Middle East and
Near East. Only in the nineteenth century did cannabis become well
known in Europe. And not until the twentieth century did it reach
the United States as a "delight giver."

"Only in America"

Cannabis was christened "marijuana" in Mexico, and around 1910
Mexican laborers began smuggling it across the border into Texas.
Why the black market preparations should have been so marketable
is puzzling, since at the time marijuana was still a constituent of
many legal proprietary medicines. Perhaps a major part of the "mental kick" from drugs is the excitement of engaging in a shady or
plainly illegal practice. In any event, the use of marijuana soon
spread to New Orleans and, according to newspaper accounts of the
1920's and 1930's, reached epidemic proportions, generating the national publicity which finally resulted in its suppression under the
1937 Marijuana Tax Act.

Most of the marijuana used in New Orleans was imported from
Havana, Tampico, and Veracruz. American and Mexican sailors were
major go-betweens, buying the drug in Mexican ports for ten to
twelve dollars a kilogram (2.2 lbs.) and selling it wholesale in New
Orleans at thirty-five to forty-five dollars a kilogram. The wholesalers
or retailers would then prepare the marijuana for distribution to cus-
tomers by a process known as "sweating," which involved soaking the
dried leaves and stems in sugar water and drying them on butcher's
brown paper. This questionable procedure was claimed to double the
strength of the drug.

Most notable is the fact that marijuana use in New Orleans was

largely confined to poor people and especially the black population. It is probably this sociological feature which accounts for the much-heralded, erroneous axiom that marijuana smoking leads to, or is closely associated with, crime.

The first major publicity to result in official action occurred in 1926, when a group of reporters wrote a series on the "marijuana menace" in the New Orleans *Morning Tribune* (10). This provoked the local police to make a flurry of investigations that resulted in wholesale arrests of peddlers and users alike. What probably caused the most public anxiety were stories in this series that a large number of *teenagers* bought and smoked "mootas," New Orleans jargon for marijuana cigarettes. The superintendent of the Children's Bureau told reporters that he felt many problem children there had come under the influence of marijuana (implicitly suggesting that marijuana made them problem children) and that two children had run away because at the Bureau they couldn't get their "muggles" (another nickname for marijuana).

At this stage only sixteen states had laws against the sale or use of marijuana, and these were loosely enforced. This, after all, was the era of prohibition and the police had more pressing matters to attend.

In the mid-1930's the city of New Orleans experienced a major crime wave. Searching for some explanation, hopefully one which might not involve police inadequacies, Frank Gomila, the Commissioner of Public Safety for the city of New Orleans, announced that:

> The crime wave unquestionably was greatly aggravated by the influence of this drug [marijuana] habit. Payroll and bank guards were doubled, but this did not prevent some of the most spectacular hold-ups in the history of the city. Youngsters known to be "muggle-heads" fortified themselves with the *narcotic* and proceeded to shoot down police, bank clerks, and casual by-standers. . . . Many of the crimes in New Orleans and the South were thus committed by criminals who relied on the drug to give them a false courage and freedom from restraint. Dr. George Roeling, coroner, reported that of 450 prisoners investigated, 125 were confirmed users of marijuana. (11)

The state narcotics officers reported that in 1936, "60 per cent of the crimes committed in New Orleans were by marijuana users." Soon newspapers throughout the country had taken up the story and given birth to a national concern.

In 1931, the Treasury Department had reported:

> A great deal of public interest has been aroused by newspaper articles appearing from time to time on the evils of the abuse of marijuana, or Indian hemp, and more attention has been focused on specific cases reported of the abuse of the drug than would otherwise have been the case. This publicity tends to magnify the extent of the evil and lends color to an inference that there is an alarming spread of the improper use of the drug, whereas the actual increase in such use may not have been inordinately large. (12)

Nonetheless, whether because of the continued newspaper publicity or an actual increase in the drug's use, the Treasury Department's Bureau of Narcotics a few years later drafted a federal law, the Marijuana Tax Act. Simultaneously, they conducted a national campaign against the drug at two levels: they worked with state legislatures in developing state laws for the regulation of marijuana; and they provided facts and figures for magazine articles about the subject. Lurid posters were distributed to alert the public to the dangers of cannabis.

Harry Anslinger, the United States Commissioner of Narcotics, pursued his job with vigor. In addition to providing information to journalists, he himself wrote articles designed to "educate" the public by terrorizing it about marijuana's adverse effects. The following quotation is from an article by Anslinger which appeared in the *American Magazine:*

> An entire family was murdered by a youthful marijuana *addict** in Florida. When officers arrived at the home they found the youth staggering about in a human slaughter house. With an axe he had killed his father, mother, two brothers, and a sister. He seemed to be in a daze. . . . He had no recollection of having committed the multiple crime. The officers knew him ordinarily as a sane, rather quiet young man; now he was pitifully crazed. They sought the reason. The boys said he had been in the habit of smoking something which youthful friends called "muggles", a childish name for marijuana. (13)

* Italics mine.

It is remarkable how many times marijuana users are referred to as "addicts" in the popular literature of the 1920's and 1930's despite medical evidence available at that time that marijuana is not addicting. As to the details of this piece of yellow journalism, it takes little psychiatric acumen to recognize that such a crime would not be committed by someone who was "ordinarily sane" and that marijuana could hardly have caused him to do it.

Soon the Federal Bureau of Narcotics went to Congress with a draft of the Marijuana Tax Act to request its passage. Marijuana smokers, then mostly underprivileged blacks, were not represented in the hearings held in Congress prior to a final vote, and the bill never faced any grave opposition. Still, vignettes from the hearings of the House Ways and Means Committee on the bill provide an interesting story. The congressmen were first assured by the assistant general counsel of the Treasury Department that the bill would in no way:

> interfere materially with any industrial, medical or scientific uses which the plant may have. Since hemp fiber and articles manufactured therefrom (twine and light cordage) are obtained from the harmless mature stalk of the plant, all such products have been completely eliminated from the purview of the bill by defining the term "marijuana" so as to exclude from its provisions the mature stalk. . . . There are also some dealings in marijuana seeds for planting purposes and for use in the manufacture of oil which is ultimately employed by the paint and varnish industry. As the seeds, unlike the mature stalk, contain the drug, the same complete exemption could not be applied in this instance. (14)

The reason that "medical uses" would not be interfered with materially was simply that the Bureau of Narcotics believed the medical profession rarely used the drug. Thus, unlike the Harrison Narcotics Act, which made morphine and related narcotics adequately available to physicians, the Marijuana Tax Act effectively ended American medical usage of cannabis.

The year of these hearings, 1937, was not too distant from the chaotic days of prohibition. Congressmen knew all too well, generally from personal experience, the difficulties provoked by the prohibition of alcohol, whose effects seemed in some ways similar to those of marijuana. Of course, there was a difference in that the congressmen were not marijuana smokers. Still, the Bureau of Narcotics made as strong a case as possible by emphasizing the grave dangers of this drug. Harry Anslinger was the star witness. He recited the tale of Hasan, Hashish, and the Assassins. He introduced a series of newspaper clippings claiming that the use of cannabis *caused* crime, addiction, and loss of *reproductive powers*. He said that cannabis use led to a "delirious rage after its administration" and that its prolonged use invariably produced "mental deterioration." He went on to cite numerous reports of "revolting crimes" which were clearly caused by marijuana use and explained that marijuana made people commit crimes because it released inhibitions, causing behavior of an "antisocial nature." He even went in for literary allusions of a low sort in his testimony: "But here we have a drug that is not like opium. Opium has all of the good of Doctor Jekyll and the evil of Mr. Hyde. This drug is entirely the monster Hyde, the harmful effect of which cannot be measured."

There were other witnesses who, in a more pallid vein, proffered reports similar to those of Mr. Anslinger. One such was Eugene Stanley, district attorney for New Orleans, whose report was entitled, "Marijuana as a Developer of Criminals." (14) He maintained that "many prosecuting attorneys in the South and Southwest have been confronted with the defense that, at the time of the Commission of the criminal act, the defendent was irresponsible, because he was under the influence of marijuana to such a degree that he was unable to appreciate the difference between right and wrong and was legally insane." District Attorney Stanley embellished the marijuana and sex story by maintaining that although the drug was commonly used as an aphrodisiac, "its continued use leads to impotency."

With such impressive testimony, the bill sailed through committee quite smoothly. Only two minor inconveniences arose during the hearings. The first had to do with the bill's provision that the seeds of the plant, as well as the flowering tops which smokers used, required prohibition because the seeds contained a small amount of the active ingredient of the drug and might possibly be used for smoking.

Strong objection to this provision came, of all places, from the bird food industry. An industrial representative appeared at the last minute in a rather excited state to reveal that the bird-seed industry at that time was using about four million pounds of cannabis seed each year. He apologized to the congressmen for appearing so late, but excused his delinquence by explaining that he and his colleagues had not realized until just then that the marijuana referred to in the bill was from the same plant providing their bird seed. He contended that inclusion of marijuana seed under the provisions of the bill would gravely damage his industry: "It is a necessary ingredient in pigeon feed, and we have not been able to find any seed that will take its place. If you substitute anything for the hemp it has a tendency to change the character of the squabs produced." Congressman Doughton of North Carolina was curious about whether pigeons got stoned on the seed: "Does that seed have the same effect on pigeons as the drug has on human beings?" The manufacturers representative answered, "I have never noticed it. But it does have a tendency to bring back feathers [which have fallen out] and improve the bird." The upshot of all this was that the government modified the bill. Since sterilized seed would do just as well for pigeon feed but could not be used to grow the plant, an amendment was introduced into the bill exempting from prohibition "sterilized seed of such plants which are incapable of germination."

A less amusing series of objections to the bill remained. The final witness was William Woodward, the legislative counsel of the American Medical Association. This organization, always extremely conservative, might well have been counted on to throw its weight behind a law to stamp out a vice which purportedly was threatening the health of the nation. Accordingly, the committee and the Narcotics Bureau must have been surprised by Woodward's testimony. He began by criticizing the committee for allowing the introduction of evidence that was grossly distorted. For instance, the statement that the Journal of the *American Medical Association* had designated marijuana "one of the problems of greatest menace in the United States" was not made by the journal itself, but was merely a quotation from Mr. Anslinger of the Bureau of Narcotics.

Woodward then proceeded to criticize those provisions of the bill which would end any further investigation of medical uses of cannabis, even though at that time cannabis was not widely used in medical practice. He was harshly critical of the committee's general procedures for obtaining evidence:

It has surprised me that the facts upon which these statements have been based [statements about the dangers of
marijuana use] have not been brought before the Committee
by competent primary evidence. We are referred to newspaper publications concerning the prevalence of marijuana
addiction. We are told that the use of marijuana causes
crime. But yet no one has been produced from the Bureau of
Prisons to show the number of prisoners who have been
found addicted to the marijuana habit. An informal inquiry
shows that the Bureau of Prisons has no evidence on that
point.

You have been told that school children are great users
of marijuana cigarettes. No one has been summoned from
the Children's Bureau to show the nature and extent of the
habit among children. And inquiry of the Children's Bureau
shows that they have had no occasion to investigate it and
know nothing particularly of it. (14)

He went on to demonstrate that the Office of Education had at that
time no evidence of any extensive use of marijuana among school
children.

Caught unawares after what had been a notably placid course of
hearings, the congressmen proceeded to badger Woodward and to
question his qualifications (he was both a physician and a lawyer and
had spent five years working in conjunction with the AMA, the Bureau of Narcotics, and the American Pharmaceutical Association
drafting a uniform narcotics act). After several angry interchanges,
committee members concluded by chastising him in a blatant self-
parody of congressional behavior: "If you want to advise us on legislation, you ought to come here with some constructive proposals
rather than criticism, rather than trying to throw obstacles in the
way of something that the Federal government is trying to do."

Needless to say, the Marijuana Tax Act, HR6385, was passed by
Congress—originally with a maximum penalty of a $2000 fine and/or
five years in prison at the discretion of the court. Until recent months
the subsequent history of the law has been one of progressive increases in its severity. In 1956 penalties were raised to the point
where sale or transfer carried a five-year mandatory sentence and a
third offence could bring prison sentences up to forty years, fines up
to $20,000, with the discretion of the judge severely hampered by
means of mandatory minimum sentence provisions.

Richard Lawrence Stack.

References

1. Julian, S.: Compt. Rend. Acad. Sci. Paris, 28:195, 1894.
2. Indian Hemp Drug Commission Report (1893), new printing, Thomas Jefferson Press, Silver Spring, Maryland, 1969, p. 492.
3. Oman, J. Campbell: *The Mystic Ascetics and Saints of India*, T. F. Unwin, London 1903.
4. Carstairs, G. M.: Quart. J. Stud. Alc., 15:220, 1954.
5. *The Book of Sir Marco Polo, the Venetian*, translated by Henry Yule, London, 1875.
6. *The Thousand Nights and a Night*, translated by R. F. Burton, Kamashastra Society, Benarĕs, 1885, Vol. 14, P. 194-224.
7. Gautier, T.: *Club des Hachichins*, Feuilleton de la Presse, 1943.
8. Dumas, Alexandre: *Le Comte de Monte Cristo*, English Edition, Fred DeFau and Company, New York, 1845 (Chapter 31, "Sinbad the Sailor").
9. Baudelaire, C.: *Les Paradis artificiels*, Paris, 1860.
10. *Morning Tribune*, New Orleans, October 17, 19, 23, and 28, 1926.
11. Gomila, F. R.: in *Marijuana: America's New Drug Problem*, by R. P. Walton, J. P. Lippincott Company, Philadelphia, 1938.
12. U. S. Treasury Department: *Traffic in Opium and Other Dangerous Drugs for the Year Ended December 31, 1931*, Government Printing Office, Washington, D.C., 1932, p. 51.
13. Anslinger, H. J., and Cooper, C. R.: American Magazine, 124:150, 1937.
14. *Taxation of Marijuana*, Hearings before the Committee on Ways and Means of the House of Representatives, 75th Congress, First Session on HR6385, April 27-30, 1937.
15. Walton, R. P.: *Marijuana, America's New Drug Problem*, J. P. Lippincott Company, Philadelphia, 1938.

⚘ behavioral effects

What is it like to be stoned on marijuana? That would seem to be a simple question, one which many readers of this book no doubt could answer readily themselves. But until quite recently it has been difficult to find objective, yet adequately descriptive, accounts of the experience within the overabundant literature on marijuana. Baudelaire, Dumas, and Gautier provided exciting, colorful, and in some ways remarkably perceptive descriptions of their hashish experiences. But they were hardly objective. By their own admission, these writers were striving to achieve the most exotic, hallucinatory experience possible, and their vivid imaginations enabled them to transform reality while under the influence of the drug far more thoroughly than most people could on marijuana. There are similar drawbacks in the modern literary accounts by enthusiasts such as Allen Ginsberg and William Burroughs. A few "rigorously controlled" studies of the effects of marijuana have been performed recently, but these hardly convey the typical subjective sensations of the average person who is smoking marijuana for pleasure in comfortable surroundings and in the company of friends. Most of the

41

laboratory investigations take place under "neutral" conditions which are sterile, cold, and predisposed to elicit pathological distortions of perceiving, feeling, and thinking. Moreover, today nearly all people have a biased mental set toward marijuana and this is well known by researchers in psychopharmocology to affect the drug experience profoundly.

A Chemist's Trip

Even now, the most straightforward, unbiased, and revealing descriptions of the drug experience are those written by a chemist thirty years ago. At that time Roger Adams had isolated from the hemp plant a mixture of tetrahydrocannabinols, chemicals whose psychotropic actions appeared to be responsible for the mind-altering effects of marijuana.* Adams's chemical studies were completed about the same time that the LaGuardia Committee investigators were performing clinical trials with prison volunteers in a hospital on New York's Welfare Island. Adams was an astute psychopharmacologist, although such a discipline did not even exist, formally, at that time. He realized that prisoners were hardly the ideal subjects for determining what effects one might expect of a psychochemical in the average citizen. Although the prisoners presumably "volunteered," Dr. Adams wondered how voluntary their choice actually was and what they might believe the experimenters would want them to say they had experienced. Moreover, most of the prisoners had previously smoked marijuana. To get a more unbiased sampling, Adams administered tetrahydrocannabinol to a dozen fellow chemists, including two members of the National Academy of Sciences. Not surprisingly, they all reacted somewhat differently, with the exception that all became hungry.

One of the most representative descriptions was provided by a university professor who, like a good scientist, maintained an hour-by-hour log of his adventure and mailed it to Dr. Adams (1):

* Though Adams narrowed down the possible "active ingredients" of marijuana to two or three tetrahydrocannabinols, another twenty-five years were to elapse before the single major psychotropic principle, delta-1-tetrahydrocannabinol (THC), was isolated and synthesized from basic chemicals.

> 5:20 p.m., took two capsules, went for a short swim, had a
> highball, and began to feel something beyond the mild glow
> from the drink about 6:15. By 6:30 felt bouncy in the knees,
> a little gay and foolish . . . 6-8:30 p.m. very much in the
> fog. Had alternate waves of hilarity and depression. Sat in
> smoking compartment looking at myself in the mirror, writing
> notes on the experiment, and feeling very silly and stupid.
> Would feel the onset of a surge of hilarity and then break
> into a raucous, rippling laugh. This gaiety was not particu-
> larly pleasant, however, as throughout I felt wholly dis-
> sociated from myself, knew I was at the mercy of the drug,
> and greatly resented this lack of control.

Typical of the physical scientist whose professional life style is directed at controlling the physical and his own subjective environment, this chemist feared a loss of control even while he was having
a good trip. He goes on to say that

> the feeling was very different from that of being at one or
> another stage of [alcoholic] intoxication, for I looked per-
> fectly clear and normal and I could stand erect without sway-
> ing and execute motions with considerable precision. I could
> not, to my annoyance as I was well aware, speak or write or
> think coherently. This bothered me particularly in the waves
> of depression when my lips would feel very parched and
> salty and I would long to break the spell and regain my own
> consciousness . . . 7:20—not so good; for a few minutes
> I sat and looked at myself in a silly way . . . this is *me*
> again. I very suddenly snapped out of it and am struggling
> back to normal. Lips are very dry, maybe I'm not quite out
> of it . . . The above is true. I am writing here in a serious
> vein—but quick, I must write that a minute or two ago I was
> sitting here in the men's lounge giggling at myself in the
> mirror saying: this stuff does make you feel pretty gay (gay
> in the neese) isn't that the damndest thing? I knew the
> spelling was wrong but couldn't write it . . . 7:42, Yes,
> snapping out again. I just had a most jubilant laugh and
> feel another coming along . . . 8:09 nearly came out of it.
> It is awful. Helpless, awful feeling. Over, over, when will it
> be over? When can I eat? . . . 8:13 a fellow just came
> in to shave. Why not? Why not at this time of the evening
> EAT . . . Ha, Ha. Now I have been silly. Looked silly . . .

Ha, Ha. Of all places to have this—the train. Bad, bad. Oh
I feel like hell, salty lips . . ."

Here the chemist has described a wave-like effect in the intensity
of symptoms—now powerful, now almost gone. That his moods
change so quickly from silly euphoria to intense anxiety is striking.
At this stage he was also beginning to feel ravenously hungry:

> At 8:30 I devoured an enormous steak dinner with great
> rapidity and thoroughness, and left no traces of any of the
> fixings, even though I ordinarily do not eat ripe olives or
> salad, and although ordinary delicacy would keep me some-
> what below the ten crackers I had with my cheese. The food
> tasted no better or worse than usual, and I had a dissociated
> feeling that my mouth was a purely mechanical guide for all
> that came its way, and wondered if mine was not very much
> the same as the "appetite" of a cat. At 9:00 I felt myself
> coming out of the spell, and again at 9:15 I felt sane for a
> minute or two. A little later the sane periods began to pre-
> dominate, and by 10 p.m. I was back again in control and
> could sit down and write out the details of a new natural
> product synthesis. Thus ended the trip. I didn't sleep too
> well or too poorly, and the next morning I felt O.K. and
> had no hang-over.

At different intervals the chemist's trip had been horrible and de-
lightful. How did he view the full experience afterwards? He told
Dr. Adams that:

> It was an interesting experiment, but I can't write too
> enthusiastic an endorsement for this drug you fellows are
> synthesizing. The feeling of well-being would not in my
> estimation equal that from about three highballs, and the
> penalty seemed to me to be pretty severe. The outstanding
> impressions were the feeling of detachment from myself and
> the extreme hunger. Are these both associated with the same
> part of the molecule? If not, you might hydrogenate out some
> of the bad effects and thereby obtain a wonderful aperitif.

This experience, while highly objective since the chemist had no
way of knowing what to expect, differs in important ways from a typical marijuana high. It was a fairly high dose of tetrahydrocannabinol, closer to hashish than marijuana, and the intensity of the ef-

fects is not typical of marijuana. Moreover, the subject seems to be the type of individual who is unwilling to let go of himself and allow the drug to take him where it may. Uptight people are notoriously prone to have bad experiences with psychedelic drugs. And, of course, even a less rigid, more receptive person experiencing so intense a drug effect with no foreknowledge and with no friends for emotional support might certainly be frightened.

College Students

While our chemist provided one of the most forthright published chronicles of being stoned, it is only the experience of a single individual. What are the most representative effects elicited by marijuana in the millions of young Americans who smoke it regularly? Charles Tart, a psychologist at the University of California in Davis (2), when starting research into the subjective effects of marijuana was surprised to find that the only information available was based on a limited number of anecdotal accounts. He began his own research by conducting informal interviews with college students to find out what marijuana intoxication was like. In two years, he collected 206 descriptions of possible effects, and assembled them into a lengthy questionnaire, which was then distributed to students who were asked to pass on the copies until they reached experienced marijuana users. In this way Tart attempted to insure anonymity. Respondents to the questionnaire were asked to say how often they had experienced each of the 206 possible effects during the preceding six months. Altogether, about 750 questionnaires were distributed. Of the 150 Californian students who returned the questionnaire, three-fourths had smoked marijuana once a week or more for periods ranging from six months to three years. By tabulating those effects which were reported to be frequent by more than half of his respondents, Tart put together a reasonably faithful picture of typical marijuana effects in contemporary experienced users. Perceptual alterations turned out to be among the most striking effects. Visual perception, according to the respondents, is altered as follows:

> I can see patterns, form, figures, meaningful designs in visual material that does not have any particular form when I'm straight, that is just a meaningless series of lines or shapes

Michael Abramson.

Michael Abramson.

> when I'm straight. When I try to visualize something I see it in my mind's eye more sharply. When looking at pictures, they may acquire an element of visual depth, a third dimensional aspect. Things are seen more sharply in that their edges, contours stand out more sharply against the background. . . . My visual perception of the space around me is changed so that what I'm looking at is very real and clear but everything else I'm not focusing on visually seems further away and otherwise less real or clear.

Clearly the drug does something that allows this smoker to focus on any perception which grasps his attention and to "groove in" completely. Aldous Huxley was entranced by the same kind of effect, but experienced it much more intensely when he took mescaline. He devoted a short book, *The Doors of Perception,* to his account of a day under the influence of the drug. With mescaline, Huxley fixated on simple things in his visual field like a table, and became so absorbed that he felt himself and all the universe to be merging with the table and becoming immanent in it. Tart's students reported effects with hearing similar to the changes in visual perception:

> When listening to stereo music or live music, the spatial separation between various instruments sounds greater, as if they were physically apart. If I try to have an auditory image, it is more vivid. With my eyes closed and just listening to sounds, the space around me becomes an *auditory* space, a space where things are arranged according to their sound characteristics instead of visual geometric characteristics. . . . I can hear more subtle changes in sounds, for example, the notes of music are purer and more distinct, the rhythm stands out more. I can understand the words of songs which are not clear when straight.

This last effect, achieving greater insight into the meaning of songs, is not actually an auditory effect, but part of the drug user's subjective sense of greater empathy and understanding of what other people say and do. Just how subjective is this sense of heightened insight has been revealed in recent experiments by Reese Jones, a psychiatrist at the University of California in San Francisco. Using objective measures of "perceptiveness," he was able to show that marijuana users, when stoned, are *less* perceptive than when sober. Upon

Vernon Shibla.

coming down from their high, his subjects regarded many of their "insights" as nonsense.

The realms of touch, taste, and smell are also intensified under the influence of marijuana: "My sense of touch is more exciting, more sensual. Some surfaces feel much smoother, silkier, while some surfaces feel much rougher, irregular and the roughness or graininess forms interesting patterns. Smells become richer and more unique. Taste sensations take on new qualities, and if I try to imagine what something tastes like, I can do so very vividly." Drug effects on taste, of course, are related to the increased appetite elicited by marijuana: "I enjoy eating very much and I eat a lot. I crave sweet things to eat like chocolate more than other foods."

Space and time perception are altered and this effect derives from both enhanced perception and altered thought processes:

> When I walk someplace my experience of the distance covered is quite changed so that distances seem to get greater, especially between me and the things or me and other people. Time passes very slowly; it's not just that things take longer, certain experiences seem outside of time, are timeless. While something is happening, I get the funny feeling that this squence has happened before in exactly the same way [Déjà vu.]

People smoking marijuana tend to estimate time intervals as almost double what they really are. Frederick Melges has recently obtained evidence from psychological experiments that this prolongation of subjective time, together with an increased concentration on the present, can account for the trance-like state of being thoroughly stoned.

Marijuana wreaks its greatest havoc or most expands the quality of existence, depending on your point of view, on thoughts and feelings:

> I appreciate very subtle humor in what my companions say, and say quite subtly funny things myself. Spontaneously, insights about myself, my personality, the games I play come to mind when stoned and seem very meaningful. These ideas are much more original. I am more willing to accept contradiction between two ideas and two views; I don't get uptight because the two things don't make immediate sense. I learn a great deal about psychological processes, general

knowledge about how the mind works. And in thinking about a problem of the sort that normally requires a series of steps to solve, I can get the answer without going through some of the usual intermediate steps.

These statements support the thesis that marijuana enhances awareness and the ability to "tie things together." Yet the same people in describing the same drug experiences also mention effects which seem contradictory: "I find it difficult to read. I do things with much less thought to possible consequences of my actions, and if I work on a problem I work less accurately as judged by later real world evaluations."

Perhaps the drug facilitates certain kinds of problem-solving, those which are most dependent on intuition, and interferes with performing tasks that require cool, analytical thinking. On the other hand, it is possible that marijuana impairs all kinds of thinking without exception and that the drug user is merely deluded in the grandiose conviction that he is doing better than ever, much as a drunk may feel that he is driving in Grand Prix style.

One area of mental functioning where even the drug user feels that something goes wrong is memory. Memory deficit has been examined in detail with rigorous psychological tests and its basis to a certain extent has been elucidated. Yet remarkably, according to both subjective accounts and objective tests, the stoned person is able to compensate for his impairment so that outside observers may not suspect that he is under any kind of drug influence:

> My memory span for conversation is somewhat shortened, so that I may forget what the conversation is about even before it is finished. I think I've said something when actually I've only thought about saying it. My memory of what went on while I was stoned is poor afterwards . . . I can continue to carry on an intelligent conversation even when my memory span is so short that I forget the beginnings of what I started to say; for example, I may logically complete a sentence even as I realize I have forgotten how it started.

This interesting interaction of impaired functioning with an act of will to overcome it is seen in the drug user's apparent loss and yet easy exertion of self-control:

Vernon Shibla.

> I find it easy to accept whatever happens, I don't need to control it or feel in control of it. I feel as if I lose control over my thoughts; they just go on regardless of what I want. I often forget to finish some task I started or get side-tracked more frequently than when straight. I giggle a lot when stoned, I am silly, even though the situation is not that funny. My inhibitions are lowered so that I do the things that I'm normally too inhibited to do, although never acts that are antisocial or morally unacceptable to myself. . . . I can come down at will if I need to be straight for a minute to deal with some complicated reality problem. I have excellent control over my fantasies; I can make them go in whatever direction I want.

Of course, the degree of self-control is a matter of dose. Several scientists have shown that with high doses of THC people have no more control of themselves than if they had taken LSD. The apparently high degree of self-control results from the fact that most marijuana users smoke the drug. Since effects come on rapidly and the dose is taken in small increments, the level of intoxication can be easily regulated.

Considering the claims made for cannabis as an aphrodisiac (Timothy Leary in this respect keeping good company with Alexandre Dumas), the comments of these college students on marijuana and sex are particularly interesting:

> Sexual orgasm has new qualities, pleasurable qualities. When making love I feel I'm in much closer mental contact with my partner; it's much more a union of souls as well as of bodies. I have no increase in sexual feeling unless it's a situation that I would normally be sexually aroused in, and then the sexual feelings are much stronger and more enjoyable. I feel as if I'm a better person to make love with when I'm stoned.

These statements are not strictly descriptive of an aphrodisiac, which would arouse sexual desire regardless of the circumstances. Rather the drug user's perception of his partner and his awareness of his own body image are sharpened, reflecting the general heightening of sensory perception under marijuana.

The students' reports confirm the already well-documented ability of marijuana to promote sleep: "I find it very easy to go to sleep at

London Daily Express.

my usual bedtime when stoned. I get very drowsy even though it's not late. My sleep is particularly refreshing if I go to bed stoned. My dreams are more vivid if I go to bed stoned."

Unlike most sleep-producing or "hypnotic" drugs, marijuana does not bludgeon its users into unconsciousness so that it can only be taken close to bedtime. The marijuana user can take the drug during the day and usually go about his business reasonably alert. When he goes to bed, however, sleep comes more readily and he tends to wake refreshed, without the hangover associated with many sleeping pills. This property of the drug is one of the major reasons that physicians of the nineteenth century prescribed it so extensively.

Most of the experiences described by Tart's subjects would fall under the heading of "good trips." This is not surprising since they were experienced smokers who knew how to regulate the effects of the drug. In this way they differed from the chemist described earlier who had no idea what to expect. Moreover, the chemist had taken a high dose of tetrahydrocannabinol by mouth so that he could do nothing to turn off the experience while marijuana smokers, if they feel themselves becoming a little too stoned, can just stop puffing. The effects will then dissipate more quickly than after ingestion by mouth.

The Weil Experiment and Opposing Results

Carefully controlled psychological experiments to delineate the nuances of the actions of marijuana on mental functioning have been extremely rare. Until quite recently scientists have been unable to obtain samples of marijuana for research despite the enormous stock piles garnered by Federal and State Bureaus of Narcotics in the course of arrests of marijuana users and sellers. During the late 1960's the hubbub over the increased use of marijuana eventuated in a slow limited distribution of drug samples to qualified investigators interested in obtaining some answers to the major controversies. Does marijuana consistently make people psychotic? Does it impair co-ordination so that the menace of millions of young people driving automobiles after smoking pot might assume the proportions of a national emergency? Does marijuana "blow people's minds" so that they cannot think rational thoughts, read clearly, or respond to questions?

With so much public concern one might expect a second La-Guardia Report or a national investigation by some blue ribbon panel. Surprisingly, one of the first thorough studies of marijuana effects had as its senior author a medical student at Harvard University, although it was conducted in a leading psychopharmacology research laboratory (3). Andrew Weil and his coworkers first decided that they would like to obtain "naïve" subjects. They placed advertisements in the student newspapers of a number of universities in the Boston area, asking for "male volunteers, at least 21 years old for psychological experiments." They eliminated non-smokers since the ability to inhale properly is crucial in getting the active ingredients of marijuana from mouth to brain. It proved extremely difficult to find marijuana-naïve persons in the student population of Boston (the experiment was performed in 1968). Despite the large number of college students in Boston and their usual interest in participating in "psychological experiments," nearly two months of interviewing were required to find nine male subjects who had never smoked marijuana. As Leo Hollister, a prominent psychopharmacologist, has remarked, "Obtaining drug-naïve subjects these days is like recruiting virgins for a black mass."

Weil and his co-authors reported that in their search for subjects:

> nearly all persons encountered who had not tried marijuana admitted this somewhat apologetically. Several said they had been meaning to try the drug but had never got around to it. A few said they had not had access to it. Only one person cited the current laws as his reason for not having experimented with marijuana. It seemed clear in the interviews that many of these persons were actually afraid of how they might react to marijuana; they therefore welcomed a chance to smoke it under medical supervision.

The experimenters also wanted to study experienced marijuana smokers. Eight heavy users of marijuana were obtained with much less difficulty. The chronic users of marijuana were needed, not only to compare their reactions with those of naïve subjects, but to "assay the quality of the marijuana that had been generously donated by the Federal Bureau of Narcotics; so as to enable the experimenters to standardize the procedure."

The first batch of marijuana supplied by the Federal Bureau of

Narcotics was judged by the experienced smokers to be no good at all. Their clinical expertise was verified by chemical measurements which showed that this batch contained very little of the active ingredient, tetrahydrocannabinol. A second, more active preparation was obtained. It was administered in the form of cigarettes and the subjects were asked to smoke two in succession. The researchers constructed a placebo by taking the outer covering of the stalks of the hemp plant, which contain almost no tetrahydrocannabinol, and chopping and rolling this material into cigarettes with a tiny plug of tobacco at one end and a plug of paper at the other so that the contents were concealed from the subjects. To mask the odor of marijuana, scented aerosols were sprayed all around the laboratory. And of course, marijuana and placebos were administered to the naïve subjects in a double blind fashion, neither experimenters nor subjects knowing who got what. Naïve subjects received two doses of marijuana, the low dose being half a gram and the high dose about two grams. The elaborate maneuvers to keep the subjects unaware of what they were smoking seem to have succeeded, since all nine naïve subjects reported that they couldn't identify the taste or smell of marijuana in the experimental cigarettes. And when they were asked to guess what they had smoked, two of them called the high dose a placebo. Interestingly, one of these two was a subject who had announced in his screening interview that he intended to "prove in the experiments that marijuana really did not do anything." Seven of the nine drug-naïve subjects, however, were able to distinguish between drug and placebo. Placebos were not given to the experienced marijuana smokers since the investigators were certain that they could not be fooled, an assumption which recent experiments by Reese Jones have shown to be questionable. The subjects were taught how to smoke the cigarettes in order to obtain maximal effects. To do this one must take a long puff, inhale deeply, and maintain the inspiration, that is, hold one's breath for about twenty seconds. About ten minutes were allowed for smoking each of the two cigarettes. In the succeeding three hours heart rate, respiratory rate, pupil size, blood glucose, and the state of the conjunctivae (the membrane lining the eyelid and exposed surface of the eyeball) were assessed, and a series of psychological tests were administered.

With the high dose of marijuana all of the experienced users became "high" by their own account and in the judgment of the experimenters. Yet, only one of the nine naïve subjects was affected nearly so intensely by the same high dose. This individual became euphoric, laughing continuously during the psychological tests. He was the one subject who said in his screening interviews that he "was extremely eager to get high because 'everyone I know is always talking about it very positively.'" That experienced users get stoned more readily than do novices is one of the tenets of marijuana mythology apparently confirmed by these experiments, but for a pharmacologist it is a peculiar and disquieting state of affairs. Drugs are usually capable of inducing tolerance or not. Either the subject becomes less and less responsive to a drug with each successive dose or he does not. If tolerance develops, then the drug user ordinarily increases his dose to maintain the same drug effect. This property is one of the major factors in making narcotic agents such as heroin addictive. But marijuana seems to produce "inverse" tolerance so that a smoker becomes more responsive with increased use and needs less to get high. What could cause this is unknown. Conceivably, experienced users are just more adept at the proper technique of inhaling the drug. Or perhaps they are so attuned to nuances of the drug effect that they can detect small amounts and then "suggest" to themselves the other aspects of intoxication.

The only notable physical changes brought about by marijuana were a slight increase in heart rate and a dilatation of the blood vessels in the conjunctivae, which results in the familiar "red eyes" of the marijuana smoker. This is probably the most efficient way of detecting whether someone is stoned.

Some of the most provocative findings emerged from the psychological tests. Several were administered. One, called the Continuous Performance Test, was designed to measure capacity for sustained attention. Subjects were placed in a dark room and told to watch a screen on which six letters of the alphabet were flashed rapidly and in a random order. The task was to press a button whenever a specified critical letter appeared. At neither dose did marijuana produce any impairment in performance of this task by either experienced or naïve subjects.

In another test more closely related to intellectual functioning, the Digit Symbol Substitution Test, subjects were presented abstract symbols equivalent to the numbers between one and nine. They were then required to translate from symbol to number with the "dictionary" of number and symbol equivalents available to them. The naïve subjects had quite a bit of trouble with this task on both the low doses and the high doses, more so with high doses, which grossly impaired their performance. The chronic users, far from displaying impaired performance, actually improved their scores with the high dose of the drug.

One other psychological test was administered. This one, referred to as the Pursuit Rotor Task, was designed to measure muscular coordination and attention. Subjects were asked to keep a stylus in contact with a small spot on a moving phonograph turntable—an appropriate task for potheads who spend so many of their waking hours beside their beloved stereo sets. On this test, just as with the digit symbol substitution test, the performance of naïve subjects fell precipitously with increasing doses of marijuana. And again the chronic users started with good base-line scores which rose after they smoked marijuana.

What are we to make of the apparent capacity of experienced marijuana users to maintain their intellectual and motor performance when they are stoned? As yet no plausible explanation has been given. To make this problem even more perplexing, we must bear in mind that the chronic drug users subjectively were more intoxicated than were the naïve subjects. One might argue that the experienced smokers suffer little impairment because they are really "tolerant" to the drug and appear to be high only because they wish the intoxication upon themselves, that is, they have "learned" psychologically how to put themselves into an intoxicated state. This is unlikely, since with the same dose of marijuana the drug brought about greater physical changes in the chronic users than in the naïve subjects. Acceleration of heart rate and red eyes were more marked in the experienced marijuana smokers. It is more likely that a person who is accustomed to the effects of marijuana can compensate fully for any drug impairment of mental or physical functioning. This would go along with the testimony of smokers who say that a marijuana high is much more manageable than alcoholic intoxication. Alcoholics do adapt and can perform better than non-drinkers when the two ingest the same amount of alcohol, but the alcoholic can never fully compensate, although he may come closer to appearing sober than a high school student who is drunk for the first time.

Even if experienced marijuana users can suppress the effects of the drug completely, this does not explain enhanced functioning. Such improvement does strain one's credulity and Weil's findings have been disputed by other investigators. Lincoln Clark, a professor of psychiatry at the University of Utah, at first was impressed with the unerring performance of marijuana subjects on psychological tests. Then he found that by choosing the appropriate task he could demonstrate considerable impairment of function (4, 5).

Like Weil, Clark had great difficulty in obtaining ideal subjects. He was afraid to seek volunteers who had never used marijuana since, in the Salt Lake City area where the University of Utah is located, many such psychopharmacologic virgins, being Mormons, would have lacked experience with intoxicants of any type. And Clark knew well from his earlier work with LSD that completely naïve subjects tolerated psychotropic drugs poorly. He was reluctant to use marijuana habitués, since so many seemed eccentric to him and were all such devout believers in the merits of marijuana that they were not likely to be reliable reporters of its effects. As a compromise, he chose for his test population psychiatry residents, medical and graduate students who used alcohol socially but had never smoked marijuana.

Many tests were administered. Since marijuana is supposed to change perception, Clark asked subjects to position vertical white rods 16 feet away from them as a measure of depth perception. Their ability to discriminate sound frequencies was also examined. He measured how long they were affected by after-images induced by spiral designs, and estimated how rapidly it was necessary to have a flickering light flicker before they perceived it as a solid light. He also used the pursuit rotor task to measure attention and muscular co-ordination. But he found no consistent marijuana-induced abnormalities in any of these tests.

Then Clark tried to estimate hand and foot reaction time to complex visual signals. Subjects had no difficulty in reacting to simple stimuli. When complicated patterns were presented, however, definite abnormalities appeared. These were not always evident in the same subjects. It seemed that the effects of the drug would wax and wane in a wave-like fashion; and when the subjects were feeling more sober, they had less difficulty with the task.

Clark was also able to demonstrate impaired performance on another test. His marijuana-ingesting subjects were asked to memorize the spatial location of ten number-coded buttons by trial and error. When all experiments were averaged, subjects performed more poorly under the influence of marijuana than when sober. As with the complex perception experiment, however, the results were highly variable. Some subjects were not affected at all, while others did well sometimes and poorly at other times. Clark concluded that the best prescription for "fouling up" someone with marijuana is to assign him a prolonged and intricate task.

Recent experiments by Glenn Kiplinger and associates using highly sensitive measures of attention and motor co-ordination support this view in showing very consistent impairment in marijuana smoking subjects (6). The difference between these studies and those of Weil and Clark lies in the greater complexity of the tasks used by Kiplinger's group. As a measure of motor co-ordination, subjects were required to duplicate complex patterns that were presented rapidly on an oscilloscope. Since the subjects' tracings were recorded and scored automatically, a slight impairment could be detected. To show abnormalities in mental performance, subjects were required to perform complicated arithmetic operations or read and comprehend selections from Aristotle. The hooker in these tests was that as subjects reported their answers verbally, their voices were played back to them with a 0.3 second delay (delayed auditory feedback) to induce anxiety and confusion.

Research results ideally should speak for themselves, but marijuana hardly represents an ideal case of scientific inquiry. The reader is free to choose from among the findings of the Weil, Clark, and Kiplinger groups those which agree with his own viewpoint. Some may wish to stress that the psychological changes Clark succeeded in demonstrating only with intricate tasks were minor and inconsistent. Others may applaud Clark in construing the variability in the drug's effects as an ominous sign and stating that "the very unpredictability of marijuana in different individuals and in the same individual at different times and under different conditions increases the risk to the user." Still others may cite Kiplinger's results as evidence that marijuana is quite predictable in doing just what Clark felt it did—fouling up the person trying to complete a complex task. Enthusiasts may choose to ignore everything except the enhanced functioning in Weil's experiment.

Marijuana, Alcohol, and Auto Driving

Those who disagree with Weil's findings on motor co-ordination might be tempted to propose special penalties for driving an automobile under the influence of cannabis. Perhaps such laws should be even more stringent than those concerned with drunken driving. Recently Alfred Crancer, chief of research at the Department of Motor Vehicles in Washington State, with a team of psychiatrists and pharmacologists, performed experiments that bear on this question (7). These investigators compared the effects of alcohol and marijuana on performance in a driving simulator apparatus.

In the simulator, the subject is seated behind a console mockup of an automobile containing standard equipment and facing a large movie screen. A driver's-eye view of the road is projected in a test film which leads the subject through normal and emergency driving situations on freeways, city and suburban streets. Driving errors are scored and broken down into categories of speeding, steering in the wrong direction, not braking, or braking at an inappropriate time, accelerating or decelerating, or failing to do either at the right time, and using the turn signal incorrectly. Previously, Crancer had shown that the driving simulator provided a valid indication of the five-year driving record of normal subjects. Individuals who made a large number of mistakes in the driving simulator tended to get involved in auto accidents and accumulate traffic violations at a high rate. The value of the simulator is further highlighted by Crancer's finding that behind-the-wheel road tests, similar to those administered to applicants for driver's licenses, were poor predictors of general driving performance.

Chronic marijuana smokers who had been getting high at least twice a month for the past six months were recruited for the experiment. Each subject was tested after smoking two marijuana cigarettes,

about the same as in Weil's experiments; after drinking enough alcohol mixed with orange juice to reach a blood alcohol concentration
of one-tenth of 1 per cent, the legal definition of drunkenness; and
with no drug treatment. The intent was to compare what happens to
a person's driving when he becomes "socially high" to a similar extent with either of the two drugs.

Results were somewhat reminiscent of those of Weil's group. Even
though subjects became quite thoroughly stoned on marijuana, in
terms of total score they performed no worse than when they were
sober. They did show somewhat more speedometer errors when under
the influence of marijuana. But the investigators pointed out that
speedometer scores do not tend to correlate with driving performance,
and are probably related primarily to the amount of time spent mon-
itoring the speedometer. In contrast, after consuming the equivalent
of about six ounces of 86 proof whiskey, there was a marked impairment in all measures of the driving simulator test, with the possible
exception of steering errors.

Does this mean that driving under the influence of marijuana is
not dangerous? Perhaps, but one must be cautious in drawing such
conclusions from Crancer's apparently well-controlled experiment.
His subjects, all enthusiastic pot smokers, probably were eager to
prove that marijuana is safe and alcohol dangerous. They could have
pushed themselves to perform especially well after smoking marijuana, better than they would normally have performed when high
on the same amount of the drug. The phenomenon that Weil described—the uncanny ability of the experienced marijuana user to
compensate psychologically for his intoxication—might account for
this. With whiskey, the subjects may have wanted to do poorly. Besides, even if they were playing fair, the large dose of alcohol may
well have been enough to make the subjects more intoxicated than
the two marijuana cigarettes had.

Not only for driving, but in any discussion of social or legal aspects, marijuana and alcohol are often mentioned in the same breath.
Since both are consumed for social purposes, one naturally wonders
how they compare in their subjective effects. The two drugs are generally looked upon as having opposite types of users—alcohol for the
hard-working, more rigid older generation, and marijuana for easy-

going, hedonistic youths. Marijuana is usually considered a mild psychedelic drug, placing it in a class with LSD. Although its effects resemble those of low doses of LSD, there are undoubtedly certain pharmacologic differences, and it is unlikely that the two drugs act at the same sites of the brain.

Reese Jones at the University of California has also compared the effects of marijuana and alcohol in human subjects (8). Since pure THC was not available, he had to use crude marijuana provided by the California state narcotics officers and thus was not sure whether he had a strong or weak batch. Even though Jones performed a crude chemical measurement of the THC content of his marijuana preparations, he was still uneasy about specification of the exact doses. Since experienced marijuana users are thought to be expert in evaluating the drug's effects and had been used by Weil for this purpose, Jones recruited as subjects ten heavy users of marijuana. These young men (average age twenty-five) qualified, if anyone does, for the designation, "pothead." They had used marijuana regularly for an average of four years or more and, at the time of the experiment, were smoking large quantities every day. After smoking marijuana or a placebo (made by extracting and discarding the THC from marijuana) they were asked to rate the quality of the drug on a zero to 100 scale, with 100 representing "the best grass you've ever had" and zero representing the worst. They rated the marijuana about 66, an average batch, which corresponded with its chemically determined THC content. But surprisingly, they judged the placebo to be just about as active (rating of 57). Jones was at a loss to explain this and wondered whether some psychoactive substance was left in the plant residue after all the THC had supposedly been extracted.

Insight into this difficulty came when he tested subjects who had head colds or just stuffy noses and found that they were considerably more accurate in distinguishing placebo from active material. Probably cues from taste and smell, which would have been the same in the placebo and active marijuana, were sufficient to "suggest" the characteristic marijuana high to the cold-free subjects, who were primed to expect it. In any event, these results serve to stress the need for caution in conducting experiments in humans with subtle psychotropic drugs like marijuana. They also suggest that marijuana peddlers—who usually respect their experienced clients' "nose for pot"—can take comfort in the knowledge that the customer, in this case, is usually wrong.

To the same experienced subjects, Jones gave enough alcohol, disguised in a fruit juice and peppermint drink, to bring their blood alcohol content to two-thirds of the "legally drunk" level. This amounted to the equivalent of a couple of martinis. In one way, alcohol and marijuana proved to have opposite effects. Whether smoked or eaten, marijuana caused subjects to overestimate time intervals, which would imply a "speeding up" of their internal clocks. In contrast, under the influence of alcohol they consistently underestimated time intervals. Thus, to a person smoking marijuana, one minute might feel like three minutes, while with alcohol it might seem as if only thirty seconds had passed. But on an information processing task alcohol and marijuana had similar effects, producing an over-all slowing of performance.

More recently Jones has obtained evidence which leads him to feel that the effects of marijuana and alcohol, as they are usually consumed socially, can hardly be distinguished. He devised an ingenious experiment to demonstrate this point. Subjects received an intravenous dose of either alcohol or saline while simultaneously smoking cigarettes which contained either plain marijuana or marijuana from which the THC had been removed. His subjects, again all chronic users, had difficulty distinguishing between marijuana and alcohol (R. Jones, personal communication). Other investigators (9) also found that marijuana and alcohol were not easily distinguished.

Whether this finding would apply to less experienced marijuana users is unknown. It certainly raises the question of whether marijuana should be classified with the psychedelic drugs—the conventional medical view—or with sedatives such as alcohol, barbiturates, and the minor tranquilizers, Miltown and Librium. The sedative classification has been espoused by at least one reputable pharmacologist (10). The answer may be that at low doses marijuana behaves like alcohol, while only at higher doses, or with more potent preparations such as hashish, are there any intimations of psychedelic or psychotomimetic properties. One might then conclude that the great majority of casual marijuana smokers use the drug for essentially the same reasons that their parents use alcohol and that only a very few veteran potheads smoke to obtain gross distortions of mental function.

Time Sense with Marijuana

Although experienced marijuana smokers have surprisingly little difficulty in coping with various types of mental gymnastics when high, everyone agrees that there is some sort of interference with mental function, even if it can be compensated for when the smokers try hard to concentrate. Students who answered Tart's questionnaire frequently described difficulty in talking to others when high, fears that they were not making sense and that they would forget what they were saying. Weil mentioned that this interference with memory seemed to be responsible for an apparently characteristic but subtle disturbance in speech: smokers would tend to go off on irrelevant tangents and their sentences were slightly disjointed. Any clear-cut, over-all disturbance in memory would have been detected on some of his psychological tests. Yet the drug could have affected a certain aspect of memory function, such as "short term" memory, which would have accounted for the subjects' troubles in getting from the beginning to the end of a sentence.

A team of psychiatrists and psychopharmacologists at Stanford University headed by Frederick Melges recently attempted to sort out different parts of memory function and determine which is most affected by marijuana (11). They administered several tests, each of which was designed to reach a different facet of memory or attention, to normal graduate students (whose experience with marijuana was confined to smoking no more than once a month) after the subjects were given THC extracted from marijuana that had been supplied by the Bureau of Narcotics and Dangerous Drugs or a placebo prepared by eliminating THC from marijuana.

In the best-known memory test used, called "serial sevens," subjects were asked to start at a number which is close to 100 and then subtract sevens serially until they passed zero. For instance, a typical sequence might proceed, 100-93-86-79-72, etc. Doing well on this test depends on "long term" memory of the simple arithmetic operations as well as sustained attention. Even high doses of THC, considerably more than a marijuana smoker usually encounters and about the amount consumed by heavy hashish users, failed to affect performance on this task.

To assess short-term memory directly, the experimenters asked the subjects to repeat a series of random digits read to them, forward or backward. Here the influence of THC became apparent. The performance of subjects receiving THC declined but was not grossly impaired, and higher doses of THC did not elicit progressive deterioration.

The test which the THC subjects definitely failed was one that involved immediate memory but also demanded that they manipulate the items recollected while holding in mind a goal of their mental operations. This sounds rather complex and abstract, but the actual test is fairly simple. Subjects were given a starting number between 106 and 114 and were asked to subtract 7, then add 1, 2, or 3 and repeat such alternate subtraction and addition until arriving at a goal somewhere between 46 and 54 specified by the experimenter. Subjects fell apart on this task, and with some of the higher doses, they still had not returned to normal performance six hours after ingesting the drug. The experimenters labeled what they saw "temporal disintegration" because the difficulty seemed related to co-ordinating memory and thinking in sequence and not just to poor memory. The subjects had special difficulty in keeping track of the goal, the target number, and as they approached it their errors became more frequent. It seemed to the investigators that this temporal incoordination of recent memories with intentions might account for the subtle but distinct disorganization of speech patterns in marijuana smokers. One of their subjects described the effect in this way: "I can't follow what I'm saying . . . can't stay on the same subject . . . I can't remember what I just said or what I want to say . . . because there are just so many thoughts that are broken in time, one chunk there and one chunk here." The loosening of verbal associations and the lack of goal-directedness appeared to be the major abnormalities in conversational patterns.

The Relation of Time Sense Changes and Other Effects

A productive researcher, Melges has continued his studies of the THC-induced "temporal disintegration," administering one test in which the subjects judged for themselves how well they were able to co-ordinate the past, present, and future as well as how "goal-directed" they felt (12). They were asked to decide whether statements like the following applied to themselves: "My past, present and future seem integrated with each other, and yet I can tell them apart"; "My sense of self-direction seems to be impaired"; "I am confident that my plans will accomplish my goals." After THC had been administered, subjects expressed the feeling that they were less able to distinguish past, present, and future and were less concerned with future goals. Some felt that their consciousness was like a movie in which the frames had slowed down so that they could "groove" on one frame at a time before moving on to the next. With peak intoxication, they would lose track of the other frames, and their stream of consciousness would progress haltingly, more like a series of lantern slides than a movie.

Melges tried to discern whether these changes in time sense were related to other marijuana effects. For instance, one effect of marijuana is the feeling that the self has become strange and unreal, which is technically called "depersonalization." This occurs even more intensely with LSD. Subjects given THC were asked to judge whether statements of depersonalization were applicable to themselves—statements like "My body seems detached as if my body and self are separated" and "I feel like a stranger to myself." With THC, subjects did describe themselves as depersonalized. Moreover, the extent of their feelings of depersonalization was closely related to the degree of their confusion of past, present, and future. Normally a person's sense of self, his sense of feeling "real," depends on knowing that he is the same person he was ten minutes and ten years ago and will be in the future. Under the influence of marijuana, a person may begin to feel unreal because he has lost the ability to locate himself in the continuum of time.

With other tests, Melges became convinced that an important factor in the disordered handling of time produced by marijuana was his subjects' tendency to focus on the present to the exclusion of the past and future. Again, he evaluated concentration on the present, past, and future by having subjects decide whether certain statements applied to themselves. These were such statements as, "I seem to live from minute to minute, with little attention to the past or future" and "I feel cut off from my past." He also asked them to judge how

Richard Lawrence Stack.

far into the future or the past they felt concerned, be it minutes, hours, or years. On THC, subjects tended to focus much more on the present. This occurred to the greatest degree in people who were having good trips and who scored high on mood factors such as pleasantness, nonchalance, egotism, and social affection.

Why harp on the "here-and-now" orientation of marijuana smokers? Because it is quite possible, according to Melges, that this could be the primary action of marijuana, giving rise to all the other known effects. It is easy to see how focusing on the present and losing touch with the past and future would impair one's immediate memory. It would also readily account for the well-documented finding that marijuana makes subjective time pass more slowly. Even more interestingly, the very vivid perceptions experienced by people smoking marijuana might well be related to their exclusive focus on the present. Isolating current experiences from the past and future would make them seem new, fresh, unexpected. Of course, one might argue that more intense perceptions come first and that these in turn cause the marijuana user to be more concerned with the present.

Marijuana is widely regarded as the chosen instrument of young people who want to drop out of society, and habitual marijuana smokers often confirm that they use the drug to free themselves from concern with the future and the past (13). Marijuana actually does help them achieve this freedom, predominantly by increasing their involvement with immediate experience. It is common knowledge that alcoholics get drunk in order to obliterate future concerns. Alcohol, however, can only do this in doses that also attenuate awareness of the present. In this way marijuana would then seem to be the more effective drug, dissolving, or at least isolating, the cares of the past and future while intensifying the present moment.

The General Picture

The mental operations of the marijuana user might be likened to a machine which is fairly resistant to breakdown provided the operator *wants it to keep running*. Performance degenerates only when subjects are required to co-ordinate thinking and memory toward a presumably desired goal. Psychological testing thus offers a sort of parallel to the stereotype of the marijuana-using younger generation held by their elders. That is, of aimless kids who cannot or will not pay attention to what is most important and, most exasperatingly, who probably could do whatever has to be done *if only they wanted to try.* The impression emerges from current research that marijuana is a mild intoxicant. Moderate users, when high, have rich fantasies and enhanced perceptions but are generally in control of their thoughts and actions and can behave quite normally if the need arises. Hallucinations and psychotic reactions can occur with prepartions of cannabis more potent than marijuana, but only rarely with marijuana itself. It is largely a question of the amount of THC swallowed or inhaled.

References

1. Adams, R., Bull. N. Y. Acad. Med., *18*: 705, 1942.
2. Tart, C. T., Nature, 226: 701, 1970.
3. Weil, A. T., Zinberg, N. E., and Nelsen, J. M., Science *162*: 1234, 1968.
4. Clark, L. D., and Nakashima, E. N., Amer. J. Psychiat., *125*: 379-84, 1968.
5. Clark, L. D., Hughes, R., and Nakashima, E. N., Arch. Gen. Psychiat. 23: 193-98, 1970.
6. Manno, J. S., Kiplinger, G. F., Haine, S. E., Bennett, I. F., and Forney, R. B. Clin. Pharm. Ther., *11*: 808, 1970.
7. Crancer, Jr. A., Dille, J. M., Delay, J. C., Wallace, J. E., and Haykin, M.D., Science, *164*: 851, 1969.
8. Jones, R. T., and Stone, G. C., Psychopharmacologia, *18*: 108, 1970.
9. Manno, J. E., Kiplinger, G. F., Scholz, N., and Forney, R. B.; Clin. Pharmacol. Ther., *12*: 202, 1971.
10. Meyers, F. in *The New Social Drug,* edited by David Smith, Prentice-Hall, Engelwood Cliffs, N. J. 1970.
11. Melges, F. T., Tinklenberg, J. R., Hollister, L. E., and Gillespie, H. K., Science, *168*: 1118, 1970.
12. Melges, F. T., Tinklenberg, J. R., Hollister, L. E., and Gillespie, H. K., Arch. Gen. Psychiat., 23: 204-10, 1970.
13. Melges, F. T., and Bolby, J., Arch. Gen. Psychiat., 20: 690-99, 1969.

✿ dangers

Is the use of marijuana and other cannabis derivatives a "dangerous" vice which should be outlawed with more or less severe legal penalties? Some specific reasons that have been put forward to justify strict legal control are that its use leads to crime, heroin addiction, sexual promiscuity, psychosis, mental deterioration, and a more subtle phenomenon called the "amotivational syndrome," purportedly a state of apathy which accounts for college drop-outs and other signs of indifference to conventional goals and mores.

The question is by no means simply academic. Smoking marijuana has become a major national pastime. The National Institute of Mental Health has provided an official estimate that between eight and twelve million persons in the United States have tried marijuana at least once. The Harris Survey estimated in 1968 that nearly fifteen million Americans were marijuana users, and almost a third of all teenagers polled answered that they or some close friends use marijuana. One national news magazine has reported that in a large number of high schools, more than half the student body has had experience with marijuana, and that its use is spreading into junior high and even elementary school.

Faced with questions about the dangers of marijuana use, scientists customarily plead that much more research is necessary before they can be answered. This, of course, is strictly true, yet many of these questions were at least partially answerable long ago. The problem is that relevant information, which began to develop from the social use of cannabis in Eastern countries over the past thousand years, has been so obscured by undocumented stories and rhetoric. Witness the following proceedings of a Senate subcommittee in 1970 reported on the front page of the *Baltimore Sun*:

> A former Army psychiatrist told a Senate subcommittee today that marijuana *caused** some American soldiers to shoot their comrades. . . . Dr. John K. Imahara, the psychiatrist, estimated that ten to twenty percent of American soldiers in Vietnam use marijuana regularly and told the Senate judiciary subcommittee on juvenile delinquency that while he was working in Vietnam a military lawyer told him about an incident in which a military helicopter began to receive gun fire at night. "The helicopter swooped down and strafed the area. The following morning American soldiers were found dead with evidence of marijuana in the guard post." He did not give any proof of the incident. He also testified about stories of bunkers being overrun and enemy breakthroughs into base camps with the evidence of marijuana cigarettes present. He testified about case histories of soldiers he examined who shot other soldiers after smoking marijuana and hearing "a voice." One soldier, with a history of smoking marijuana picked up a pistol, shot a lieutenant colonel he had never seen before and then calmly put the pistol down, "as though fulfilled that he had done what the voice told him to do," Dr. Imahara said. (1)

* Italics mine.

The reporter stated that Imahara gave no proof of the helicopter incident, that it was no more than hearsay, yet the report was entitled "GI Slayings Tied to Drugs" and made no mention of the well-established fact that marijuana smoking certainly does not *cause* people to hear voices and commit murder. Indeed, in the same newspaper article it was stated that Senator Thomas Dodd then "theorized that drug usage played a major role in the alleged 1968 My Lai massacre of civilians by American troops."

The Indian Hemp Commission

In India in the nineteenth century three forms of cannabis—bhang, ganja, and the more potent charas—were widely used. In certain of the Indian states, charas was subject to special taxes, while bhang could be manufactured and distributed throughout India with no legal restrictions. In 1893, the Secretary of State for India asked the British government to appoint a commission to investigate all facts about the cultivation, trade, and preparations of hemp drugs in India, the effect of their use on social and moral conditions of the people, as well as the desirability of regulating the growth and sale of these products. Norman Taylor has advanced the theory that England's motive was to inquire into the possibility of declaring cannabis use illegal and replacing it with the custom of drinking good Scotch whisky, from which a large tax revenue could be derived (2).

At any rate, a seven-member commission, consisting of four British and three Indian officials, was set up and worked full time for over a year, receiving evidence from more than a thousand witnesses, including over three hundred physicians. They made field trips to thirty cities. They thoroughly analyzed the records of judicial proceedings regarding cases in which hemp drugs were a factor, as well as the files of every mental hospital in India. Their report was a massive tome including six large volumes of appendices. It is without a doubt the most exhaustive study of marijuana ever performed (3).

The commission investigations were conducted with typical British impartiality. In giving his charge to the commission, the Secretary of State emphasized the caution with which different factors should be weighed in making a value judgment about the disposition of cannabis. He warned that prohibition or repressive measures might "be resented as an unjustifiable interference," that the people might be driven to use more deleterious drugs, and that laws might be impossible to enforce.

The commission initially heard anecdotes about the capacity of cannabis to produce mental aberration. Records of insane asylums listed large numbers of patients suffering from "hemp psychosis." The members, however, were not satisfied with such indirect evidence. They asked what the exact criteria were for determining that a given patient's psychosis were *caused* by cannabis. As they analyzed each case of apparent "hemp drug insanity," it became more and more apparent that the evidence for a causal link between the use of hemp drugs and mental illness was tenuous at best. The commissioners later wrote:

> The popular idea that the use of hemp drugs may induce insanity can be traced back for many centuries and the present day views on this subject are no doubt the outcome of old popular ideas which have been handed down and become concrete. With non-medical witnesses the mere use of the drug along with the fact of insanity, as the evidence shown, has as a rule been accepted as cause and effect. Of the large number of medical witnesses who had given evidence before the Commission, probably not a single one has ever observed the inception of the habit and the use giving rise to mental aberration, and been in a position to gauge the value of other contributory causes if present. . . . The careful inquiry which has been made by the Commission into all the alleged hemp drug cases admitted in one year into asylums in British India demonstrates conclusively that the usual mode of differentiating between hemp drug insanity and ordinary mania was in the highest degree uncertain, and therefore fallacious.

The commission did maintain that excessive use of hemp drugs could intensify mental instability and even lead to insanity. This judgment applied to the chronic charas smokers, often unemployed, whose lives centered on the drug and who would nowadays be called "heads." But the commissioners felt that the mental deterioration alleged to result from hemp drug use had been greatly exaggerated.

In assessing the relationship between cannabis and crime, the commission again found gross deficiencies in the supporting evidence. They concluded that the association was not likely to be causal but instead that:

> Consumers of hemp drugs are found more among the lower orders, among the poor, than among the more wealthy. The former are, of course, the classes to which . . . bad characters belong. This is the explanation of the alleged fact

that proportionately more consumers of hemp drugs are to be found among bad characters than among the whole population. But the general opinion is that hemp drugs have *per se* no necessary connection with crime.

After two years of deliberation the commission concluded that no effects of the drug were sufficiently adverse as to warrant prohibition of its use. A system of regulation by licensing and taxation was recommended, much like the Federal regulations in the United States for alcoholic beverages. In these recommendations, distinctions were made between bhang, ganja, and charas, with heavier taxes recommended for charas. In quite recent years, charas has finally been banned in India.

The findings of the Indian Hemp Commission, while thorough and reliable, are only applicable to India in the nineteenth century. For a drug whose effects are so profoundly determined by the user's attitude and the setting, comparable data for the United States are needed. Such an American "Hemp Commission Report" is indeed available, at least for the City of New York in the 1930's (4).

The LaGuardia Report

In 1938, newspapers in New York and many other large cities were printing lurid stories about the "killer drug," marijuana. Rather than merely mouthing slogans about law and order, Mayor LaGuardia appointed a committee of scientists to find out what the scope of the problem in New York City was. After discussions with consultant scientists and representatives of many departments of the city government, the Committee could come to no conclusion as to the effects of marijuana upon psychological and physiological functions of man. Nor could they find any reliable information about the actual extent of marijuana use in New York City. Accordingly, they designed two studies.

The first was sociological; it focused on the extent of marijuana smoking, how the drug was obtained, in what districts, among what races and classes, whether particular social conditions were related to its use, and how marijuana use was related to criminal or antisocial acts. The second study was a clinical trial to examine the psychological and physiological effects of the drug in human subjects, and to determine whether the drug produced physical or mental deterioration, and whether it might have therapeutic use in the treatment of disease.

In the clinical study, seventy-two prison volunteers were hospitalized at the Welfare Island Hospital for about a month and were administered an extract of marijuana or given marijuana cigarettes to smoke. Nine of the subjects, seven men and two women, experienced what were referred to as psychotic episodes. Actually, six of the nine experienced only what might be called "bad trips," with intense anxiety and restlessness which subsided in a few hours. Of the remaining three, one was an epileptic who experienced a seizure after smoking a marijuana cigarette. Upon recovering from the seizure he reported having had visions of angels and choirs singing as he had lapsed into unconsciousness. This would hardly qualify as a "psychotic episode," and it is unclear whether the epileptic fit was precipitated by marijuana or was merely coincidental. On another occasion the same subject became vaguely paranoid after receiving an extract of Adams's semi-purified tetrahydrocannabinol, but he recovered after four days.

Another subject, a female, became depressed a few days after taking marijuana. Her depression cleared after several weeks. Its relationship to marijuana was unclear, as she had also been using heroin extensively.

In the third subject, the association of psychosis with marijuana ingestion was even more tenuous since he did not become overtly disturbed until two weeks after his return to the penitentiary, when he developed symptoms characteristic of schizophrenia.

The researchers and even the Commissioner of Correction for the City of New York, Dr. Peter Amoroso, were impressed with the low incidence of adverse effects. Amoroso commented, "I am indeed surprised that we had so little trouble with our volunteers upon completion of their study and sojourn at Welfare Hospital, and the few psychotic episodes that occurred are exactly what we would expect in the whole group without considering the administration and effects of excessive doses of marijuana."

To ascertain if there were any mental or physical deterioration, about sixty prisoners on Ward's Island who had been smoking marijuana daily for periods of two to sixteen years, were compared with non-users. A complete physical and neurological examination and blood and urine laboratory tests were performed. Careful psychiatric examination was directed at reviewing orientation, intelligence, knowledge, judgment, and abnormal mental content. Intelligence tests were administered. There was no difference in I.Q. scores between users and non-users. Among the heaviest users, seventeen men who had smoked an average of six cigarettes a day for the past six years, there were no abnormal mental or physical findings which could differentiate them from non-users. Thus, the investigators concluded that there was no apparent mental or physical deterioration as a result of the use of marijuana.

The sociological investigation was carried out by six police officers from the narcotics squad who dressed in civilian clothes and lived in the environment of marijuana use and peddling. They found that marijuana was used largely by lower class, black, unemployed individuals, and that users would consume about six to ten cigarettes a day. Smokers were quite aware of the amount they desired in order to get "high" and would not smoke any more than was necessary to reach this level. In fact, there was a certain apprehension about getting "too high." If this happened, users would try to "come down" with beer or soda pop or a cold shower. Interestingly, smokers maintained that the effects of the drug were negated by drinking whiskey, which was therefore avoided when smoking marijuana.

To attack the question of marijuana use among school children, the Committee made an extensive survey of elementary, junior high, and high schools. Principals and school teachers were interviewed, schools were observed directly and any complaints made by parents were investigated. The Committee concluded that, "Although marijuana smoking may be indulged in by small numbers of students in certain schools of New York City, it is apparently not a widespread or large scale practice."

In writing their report, the members of the Committee were quite emphatic about the relationship between marijuana and opiate addiction:

> We have been unable to confirm the opinion expressed by some investigators that marijuana smoking is the first step in the use of such drugs as cocaine, morphine, and heroin. The instances are extremely rare where the habit of marijuana smoking is associated with addiction to these other narcotics.

The general conclusions of the sociological study were unequivocal in debunking the myths that had been given so much publicity. Their decisive clarity is a gem among scientific studies which often waver and hedge interminably before drawing definite conclusions:

1. Marijuana is used extensively in the Borough of Manhattan but the problem is not as acute as it is reported to be in other sections of the United States.

2. The introduction of marijuana into this area is recent as compared to other localities.

3. The cost of marijuana is low and therefore within the purchasing power of most persons.

4. The distribution and use of marijuana is centered in Harlem.

5. The majority of marijuana smokers are Negroes and Latin Americans.

6. The consensus among marijuana smokers is that the use of the drug creates a definite feeling of adequacy.

7. The practice of smoking marijuana does not lead to addiction in the medical sense of the word.

8. The sale and distribution of marijuana is not under the control of any single organized group.

9. The use of marijuana does not lead to morphine or heroin or cocaine addiction, and no effort is made to create a market for these narcotics by stimulating the practice of marijuana smoking.

10. Marijuana smoking is not the determining factor in the commission of major crimes.

11. Marijuana smoking is not widespread among school children.

12. Juvenile delinquency is not associated with the practice of smoking marijuana.

13. The publicity concerning the catastrophic effects of marijuana smoking in New York City is unfounded.

Unfortunately, the Mayor's Report did not make a deep or lasting impression upon public opinion. The conclusions were obviously not what some people wanted to hear. As soon as the results began to appear in 1942, they were vigorously attacked. Harry Anslinger, the major proponent of the banning of marijuana, criticized the conclusion of the psychiatric investigation that the "prolonged use of the drug does not lead to physical, mental or moral degeneration, nor have we observed any permanent deleterious effects from its continued use" (5). He wrote a letter to the *Journal of the American Medical Association* protesting that such statements were harmful to the primary interest of the Bureau of Narcotics, which "is the enforcement aspect." Despite the eminent position in American medicine of many of the members of the Mayor's Committee, the *Journal of the American Medical Association* in an editorial also attacked the report:

"For many years, medical scientists have considered cannabis a dangerous drug. Nevertheless a book called *Marijuana Problems* by the New York City Mayor's Committee on marijuana submits an analysis by seventeen doctors of tests on 77 prisoners and, on this narrow and thoroughly unscientific foundation, draws sweeping and inadequate conclusions which minimize the harmfulness of marijuana. [It was absurd for the *Journal* to criticize the LaGuardia Report on such grounds, since the articles it published at that time were usually authored by only one or two doctors and were often based on only a handful of case reports, rarely investigating with care more than a dozen patients.] Already the book has done harm. One investigator has described some tearful parents who brought their 16-year-old son to a physician after he had been detected in the act of smoking marijuana. A noticeable deterioration had been evident for some time even to their lay minds. The boy said he had read an account of the LaGuardia Committee Report, and that this was his justification for using marijuana. The book states unqualifiedly to the public that the use of this narcotic [at least the *Journal of the American Medical Association* should have had enough sophistication to distinguish marijuana from a narcotic] does not lead to physical, mental or moral degeneration and that permanent deleterious effects from its continued use were not observed in 77 prisoners. . . . Public officials will do well to disregard this unscientific, uncritical study and continue to regard marijuana as a menace wherever it is purveyed" (6).

Besides its unfortunately vindictive tone, this editorial misrepresented the findings of the Mayor's Committee. Although the report had concluded that prolonged use was not associated with deleterious effects in the prisoners they examined, it explicitly stated that under certain conditions the drug could cause psychotic reactions. In fact it perhaps went too far in labeling as "psychotic episodes" six cases where there was a high level of anxiety and disorientation but which lasted only for the few hours of the drug experience. In conventional psychiatric terminology such reactions are not usually labeled "psychotic."

The findings of the LaGuardia report were quite similar to those of the Indian Hemp Commission, which is impressive considering the profound cultural differences and the fifty years separating the two studies. It suggests that the results of both investigations might apply to the contemporary American experience. However, certain aspects of the use of marijuana in the United States today are so closely related to current social conditions that a close examination of the most recent literature available is warranted. One cardinal example is the relationship of marijuana to heroin use. Another is marijuana's role in the peculiar ennui which leads youths to drop out of conventional society, which might be a sign of serious emotional disturbance.

Marijuana and Heroin

The idea that marijuana use leads to heroin addiction is relatively new. In the 1930's even the most virulent anti-marijuana publicists failed to stress any relationship between the two. For instance, in its pamphlet "Marijuana or Indian Hemp and Its Preparations," the International Narcotics Education Association had many devastating comments to make about marijuana but did not mention an association with heroin addiction:

> The narcotic content in marijuana decreases the rate of heart beat and causes irregularity of the pulse. [What narcotic content? Actually marijuana increases the pulse rate.] Death may result from the effect upon the heart. [Also not true. Marijuana is one of the least toxic drugs known and has never been reported to be fatal in man.] Prolonged users of marijuana frequently develop delirious rage which sometimes leads to heinous crimes such as assault and murder. Hence marijuana has been called the "killer drug." The habitual use of this poison *always* causes a very marked mental de-

terioration and sometimes produces insanity. . . . While the marijuana habit leads to physical wreakage and mental decay, its effects upon character and morality are even more devastating. The victim frequently undergoes such degeneracy that he will lie and steal without scruples; he becomes utterly untrustworthy and often drifts into the underworld where, with his degenerate companions, he commits high crimes and misdemeanors. Marijuana sometimes gives man the lust to kill unreasonable and without motive. Many cases of assault, rape, robbery and murder are traced to the use of marijuana. (7)

During the congressional hearings preceding passage of the Marijuana Taxt Act of 1937, Harry Anslinger, for thirty-two years the Director of the Bureau of Narcotics (he is to narcotics what J. Edgar Hoover is to the FBI), did not at that time see any relationship between the use of marijuana and of heroin. When asked if the marijuana smoker was likely to graduate to the use of opiates, narcotics, or cocaine, he replied, "No sir, I have not heard of a case of that kind. I think that it is an entirely different class. The marijuana addict does not go in that direction." (8) Moreover, when testifying a few weeks later before a different subcommittee he re-emphasized these remarks: "There is an entirely new class of people using marijuana. The opium user is around 35 to 40 years old. These [marijuana] users are 20 years old and know nothing of heroin or morphine." Yet, when asked about the association of the two drugs eighteen years later, Mr. Anslinger replied, "That is the great problem and our great concern about the use of marijuana, that eventually if used over a long period, it does lead to heroin addiction." Was Mr. Anslinger confused, or had the patterns of drug use changed?

A great deal of literature in the 1950's and 1960's emphasizes the link between marijuana and the opiates. In an official United States Bureau of Narcotics publication published in 1965, the following advice is offered to the young:

> It cannot be too strongly emphasized that the smoking of the marijuana cigarette is a dangerous first step on the road which usually leads to enslavement by heroin. . . . Ordinarily a person is tempted first with marijuana cigarettes. He may not even know they are dope. Then someone usually

already addicted makes it easy to try some heroin. Most teen-age addicts started by smoking marijuana cigarettes. *Never let any one persuade you to smoke even one marijuana cig-arette. It is pure poison.* (9)

What might have led to an increased association of heroin and marijuana in the years following 1937? It is tempting to speculate that the Marijuana Tax Act, by making the sale and possession of the drug crimes with stiff penalties, enhanced the likelihood that deal-ers in heroin would branch out into marijuana. This result was prophesied by Earle Albert Rowell, a zealous reformer who cam-paigned throughout the country for over twenty years against the evils of alcohol, tobacco, and marijuana. In his book, *On the Trail of Marijuana: The Weed of Madness,* a classic of wild hyperbole, he described the following conversation with a heroin dealer:

> He was a shrewd gangster looking to the future.
> "Marijuana is the coming thing," he declared.
> "But," I protested in surprise, "Marijuana is not habit forming like morphine or heroin; and besides it's too cheap to bother with."
> He laughed. "You don't understand. Laws are being passed now by various states against it and soon Uncle Sam will put his ban on it. The price will then go up, and that will make it profitable for us to handle. . . . Marijuana is not an end in itself, it is too unreliable, its effects are too un-predictable. The marijuana user is not a continuous daily customer. . . . But it is a perfect missing link. . . . While there is some money in marijuana it is not worth our bother-ing with except as a key to morphine or heroin. We are experimenting to find the best method of switching from reefers to opiates." (10)

There may be some truth in Rowell's conjectures. Researchers for the LaGuardia Committee could find no association in 1939 of mari-juana and heroin use. However, recent studies have shown some link. We must bear in mind that even if heroin users formerly were mari-juana users, this does not establish that marijuana *caused* them to become heroin addicts. Moreover, people in various socio-economic strata smoke marijuana, and a relationship between the two drugs in one class may not hold in another. This important point is borne out

in a recent survey performed by two criminologists, J. C. Ball and
C. G. Chambers.

These researchers studied over 2000 heroin addicts admitted to the
United States Narcotics Hospitals at Lexington and Fort Worth
during 1965. They included both voluntary admissions and federal
prisoners, middle class as well as lower class, black as well as white
addicts. Each newly admitted patient was asked 1) whether he had
ever used marijuana; 2) at what age he was first arrested; 3) at what
age he first used opiates; 4) what drugs he used at present; 5) what
method of administration he used; and 6) from whom drugs were
obtained.

Ball and Chambers found two quite distinct patterns of opiate use.
The first involved large metropolitan states such as New York, Illinois, California, and Texas, in which there was a high incidence of
drug addiction, usually to heroin. In these states, more than 50 per
cent of the heroin addicts had used marijuana as well as opiates. On
the other hand, in twelve states, which were predominantly in the
South, such as Virginia, North Carolina, and South Carolina, most
addicts used opiates other than heroin and only rarely used marijuana
as well.

In personal interviews with over 300 of the patients, Ball and
Chambers found the most frequent pattern of association between
the two drugs to be onset of marijuana smoking at about age seventeen, arrest about age nineteen, and the beginning of heroin use at
twenty. Certainly marijuana use commonly *preceded* heroin. However, since hardly any addicts from southern states began with marijuana, clearly marijuana was not a *necessary* link in the onset of
opiate addiction.

In the course of their extensive interviews, Ball and Chambers
found several factors that might account for the connection. The
two drugs were thought to produce a similar "high." Both drugs
were obtained from the same underworld sources of supply. The
neighborhood friends with whom marijuana use began were usually
the same friends who introduced the incipient addict to the use of
heroin.

What about the prophecy of Earle Rowell in 1937 that banning
marijuana would be followed by an increased association of opiate
addiction and marijuana use? Ball and Chambers addressed them-

selves to this question by tabulating the age of heroin addicts with or without a history of marijuana use. The average age of marijuana-using heroin addicts was twenty-nine while for those who had never smoked marijuana, it was forty. Rowell may have been right.

Another way of assessing the relationship between marijuana and heroin is by analyzing trends of drug use. If marijuana is indeed a stepping stone to heroin, the rapid escalation in its use in recent years should be associated with a comparable increase in heroin addiction. John Kaplan recently analyzed the data of arrests for heroin and marijuana possession and sale in California in the 1960's (12). He observed that between 1960 and 1968, while arrests for marijuana rose more than 700 per cent, those involving heroin fell about 7 per cent.

There are places in the world where a high incidence of opiate addiction occurs with little marijuana use. Vancouver, British Columbia, is known to have the second highest heroin addiction rate outside the Orient, and until very recently marijuana has been almost unknown there. In Hong Kong, where the incidence of opiate addiction is the highest in the world, the only chronic marijuana users are American tourists.

Dependence, Dissipation, and Dementia

There is some concern today that marijuana may provoke "psychological dependence," making it difficult for heavy smokers to give up their habit. Such dependence can occur with innumerable substances consumed and activities indulged in by man and with marijuana it is hardly a cause for worry. Donald Louria estimates that no more than between 2 and 5 per cent of marijuana smokers become potheads (13), which is much lower than the dependency rate for alcohol and tobacco.

A more serious concern is that young marijuana smokers may become dropouts from society, afflicted with the "amotivational syndrome." As already discussed, this is a well-documented sequel of chronic, heavy ingestion of hashish or charas. Constantine Miras has given the following description of this syndrome in Greece:

> Heavy hashish smokers after 15 to 20 years are usually out of the community. This is due to laziness, psychic instability,

amorality, and loss of drive and ambition. They have rather apathetic faces of a grayish-yellow color. . . . They all look much older for their age, are slim and in very poor health. They speak and move very slowly in a peculiar way. (14)

Miras emphasized in a recent meeting on drug abuse that these debilitated individuals constituted only a small percentage of those who habitually smoked hashish.

Most of the data bearing on chronic effects of cannabis comes from the mental hospital statistics of the Near Eastern countries and India. These are notoriously unreliable and it is virtually impossible to distinguish between mental disturbance caused by organic abnormalities in the brain and so-called functional psychosis. At best, one might try to ascertain if any mental illness is definitely associated causally with heavy use of cannabis.

Chopra and Chopra examined records of patients in all of the major mental hospitals in India in the decade of the 1930's, and were able to come up with between 400 and 600 cases in which they felt mental disturbance was attributable to cannabis (15). This is not a large number considering the huge population of India and the fact that cannabis was routinely listed as a cause of mental disturbance in hospitals. Moreover, it is difficult to tell if the Chopras' could distinguish whether cannabis produced insanity or merely led to the gradual social and emotional disintegration which in turn provided a fertile ground for the development of psychosis.

A study by Benabud is widely quoted by those who claim that cannabis use leads to mental deterioration. Benabud examined the records of all the patients admitted in 1956 to a 2000-bed mental hospital in Morocco (16). His finding that two-thirds of the patients in the hospital were marijuana smokers has sometimes been taken as *prima facie* evidence that marijuana use causes mental illness. Of course, one must bear in mind that a large proportion of the Moroccan populace of the socio-economic strata from which the mental institution draws its patients are frequent marijuana users. Benabud felt that in four-fifths of the marijuana-smoking patients, the drug contributed in some way to their mental illness. However, he made no analysis to discern whether the role of marijuana was ever more than that of a precipitating or an aggravating factor in a pre-existing condition.

The Wootton report, product of an extensive evaluation of the cannabis literature by a commission of the British House of Lords in 1968, concluded that "no reliable observations of such a syndrome [of mental deterioration due to cannabis] have been made in the Western World, and that from the Eastern reports available to us, it is not possible to form a judgment on whether such behavior is directly attributable to cannabis-taking." (17)

Adverse Mental Effects in the United States

Since marijuana use has been a middle-class phenomenon in the United States for only a few years, very little is known of its chronic effects; even acute adverse reactions have not yet been systematically evaluated in terms of incidence and relative severity. There have, however, been a number of anecdotal accounts of marijuana reactions as well as a growing set of general impressions among clinicians who deal regularly with marijuana users as to the frequency, prognosis, and treatment of these reactions.

In evaluating reports of panic reactions or psychoses following marijuana use, it is critical to determine whether a) the drug only precipitated mental breakdown in an already unstable personality; b) the adverse reaction occurred in an experienced user or a naïve subject ill-at-ease about the legal or social implications; or c) the case was a bonafide drug reaction.

It is well established that high enough doses of THC will uniformly produce psychotomimetic effects in man fairly similar to the effects of LSD. But the average marijuana smoker consumes less than one-twentieth the amount of THC needed to give rise to psychotomimetic actions. Accordingly, one might expect a true marijuana psychosis to be rare. Indeed, David E. Smith, medical director of the Haight-Ashbury Medical Clinic in San Francisco, has written:

> At San Francisco General Hospital 5000 acute drug intoxications were treated in 1967. Despite the high incidence of marijuana use in San Francisco, no "marijuana psychoses" were seen. In fifteen months of operation the Haight-Ashbury Clinic has seen approximately 30,000 patients—visits for a variety of medical and psychiatric problems. Our research indicated that at least 95 per cent of the patients had

used marijuana one or more times, and yet no case of primary marijuana psychosis was seen. (18)

Smith felt that most cases of panic or psychotic reactions following marijuana use were determined largely by situational factors, that they were not caused by the drug's mind-altering effects, but by the patient's fright on realizing that his mental functioning has changed. He had seen only three cases of psychosis that he considered to be induced by marijuana, and the individuals, a reporter and two doctors, were very much alike:

> They were all successful members of the establishment, in their middle thirties, and were using marijuana for the first time in "far out" environments. All had extreme paranoid reactions characterized by fear of arrest and discovery, and two of three were hospitalized in private hospitals under a "non-drug" psychiatric diagnosis.

Cases of apparent marijuana psychosis occurring in soldiers in Vietnam have been reported (19). Because of the wartime setting, the authors were reluctant to relate them to adverse reactions in the United States.

Andrew Weil, who performed one of the most useful recent experiments examining the psychological effects of marijuana, also emphasized that panic reactions depend on expectations (20). In his experience, panic reactions constitute more than 75 per cent of all adverse reactions to the drug. As evidence of the important environmental factor, he cites the fact that such effects vary tremendously in frequency from one setting to another. In colleges where marijuana is given casual acceptance, he found that fewer than 1 per cent of users panicked, whereas in a rural southern college, where experimentation with the drug represented a considerably greater degree of social deviance, 25 per cent of first users had panic reactions.

Panic states sometimes may be so severe that they seem to have psychotic proportions. However, these are usually not true "drug psychoses," especially when occurring in individuals with no previous history of mental illness. Since they often take the form of fear that the subject might lose his mind, Weil recommended that the best therapy is simple reassurance, *not* hospitalization or tranquilizers. He described several cases of panic handled by physicians who made the diagnosis of "acute psychotic reaction" and treated the patients as if they were experiencing a schizophrenic psychosis, only to have the patients' condition worsen. When a physician more knowledgeable about marijuana subsequently stopped the tranquilizing medication and calmly explained to the patient that he was merely experiencing an "unusually strong marijuana high" and that there was no danger of becoming psychotic, the panic abated within a few hours.

An adverse effect which causes great concern because of its unpredictable character is spontaneous recurrence of the drug effect, more popularly known as "flashbacks." Flashbacks are well-documented phenomena after LSD ingestion. They are most commonly manifested as an awareness that one's perception of self and the environment has momentarily reverted to what it was during the initial drug experience. Sometimes, however, flashbacks can assume psychotic dimensions and persist for many hours. LSD flashbacks rarely precipitate complete mental breakdown. Recently, a team of psychiatrists at the University of North Carolina reported four cases in which psychic effects of marijuana recurred up to a few days after smoking the drug (21). The authors emphasized that in two of the cases, the flashbacks were mild and pleasurable, hence should not be looked on as adverse reactions. In the other two, the recurrence of a "strange feeling" about the self as well as altered perception of the environment precipitated considerable anxiety. One patient was hospitalized for a few days until symptoms dissipated, while the other returned to normal after receiving tranquilizers and supportive psychotherapy for a week.

At the Haight-Ashbury Clinic, the recurrence of marijuana effects is almost unknown, although flashbacks from LSD and other psychedelic drugs are common. Quite frequently, however, marijuana may precipitate a flashback to a previous LSD experience. In Weil's experience, flashbacks to marijuana or to LSD experiences usually are benign and gradually fade out as the hallucinogenic episode recedes in time.

Perhaps the most serious adverse mental effect of marijuana and of all psychedelic drugs is the precipitation of functional psychoses. In these cases, all observers agree that the psychosis is not a direct product of the drug. Rather, in an individual whose psychic organization is already unstable, the drug triggers a breakdown. It is difficult to estimate the frequency of such cases, since the incidence will depend on the relative proportion of drug users who harbor latent psychological disorder. In these patients the course of the illness is not related to drug dosage but to the nature of the psychosis involved, whether it be schizophrenic or depressive, mild or severe. A key question not so readily answered about these patients is whether the breakdown would have been averted had the patient not taken the drug.

Another possibly serious consequence of marijuana use is the so-called "amotivational syndrome." Simply defined in the contemporary United States, this refers to youths who regularly use marijuana, usually with many other psychoactive drugs, and concurrently lose the desire to work or compete. How many young Americans are afflicted with this "disease"? The loose designation can probably be applied with confidence to all inhabitants of "counter-culture" communities, ranging from Haight-Ashbury, Berkeley, and the East Village in New York to the communes scattered throughout the countryside. Conservatives perhaps would be inclined to include also half of today's college students.

Unquestionably there is a close association of dropping-out from society and turning-on with drugs. But it is difficult to tell which experience is primary. Marijuana has been available for at least sixty years in the United States. Why the epidemic of its use now? Perhaps social forces have led to a generation of dropouts and drug use is only secondary. Amotivational youths have possibly espoused marijuana because it suits their predominant *Weltanschauung* rather than vice versa. They undoubtedly consider the straight world to be passing up a good thing and would scoff at such a dignified label as "amotivational syndrome."

Conclusions

It is important to appreciate the difference between marijuana and hashish. The acute dangers of smoking marijuana are quite limited. Some people, probably only a small percentage, experience severe anxiety and paranoia which, however, are usually only short lived. Hashish, on the other hand, can probably be as hallucinogenic and psychotomimetic a drug as LSD. Although there have been few reports of catastrophic sequelae to bad hashish trips in the United States, we might begin hearing horror stories similar to the LSD reports were hashish use to become more widespread.

Marijuana is definitely not physically addicting in the sense that the opiates are addictive drugs. No one would deny that marijuana users are "psychologically dependent" on their drug. But such dependence is hardly more severe than the need for a morning cup of coffee.

Of greater concern is the question of long-term effects of cannabis drugs. The "stepping-stone to heroin" theory has been pretty much debunked. It seems likely that the association between the two drugs is due simply to their being sold by the same peddlers.

The Indian experience suggests that moderate social use of marijuana corresponding to the American habit of social drinking is unlikely to have grave harmful consequences. The pothead, however, may be running greater risks. Certainly many chronic smokers in the Near East become derelicts of society, suffering physical and mental deterioration. It is not so clear what fate will be in store for American potheads who have dropped out of school, work, and conventional society. We cannot even say with assurance whether their lack of motivation is the product or the cause of their love-affair with marijuana.

References

1. "GI Slayings Tied to Drugs," Baltimore *Sun,* August 20, 1970, p. 1.
2. Taylor, N.: *Narcotics—Nature's Dangerous Gifts,* Dell Publishing Co., New York, 1970, p. 26.
3. *Marijuana: Report of the Indian Hemp Drugs Commission 1893-1894,* Thomas Jefferson Publishing Company, Silver Spring, Maryland, 1969, p. 250.
4. Mayor's Committee on Marijuana: The Marijuana Problem in the City of New York, Jacques Cattel Press, Lancaster, Pennsylvania, 1944, p. 13.
5. Allentuck, S., and Bowman, K. M.: Amer. J. Psychiat., *99:* 248-51, 1942.
6. Editorial, J. Amer. Med. Assoc., *127:* 1129, 1945.
7. *Marijuana or Indian Hemp and its Preparations,* International Narcotics Education Association, Los Angeles, 1936.

8. Lindesmith, A. R.: *The Addict and the Law,* University of Indiana Press, Indianapolis, 1965, p. 231.

9. *Living Death: Truth About Drug Addiction,* U.S. Treasury Department, Bureau of Narcotics, Government Printing Office, Washington, D.C., 1965.

10. Rowell, E. A., and Rowell, R.: *On the Trail of Marrijuana: The Weed of Madness,* Pacific Press, California, 1939, p. 69.

11. Ball, J. C., and Chambers, C. G.: J. Criminal Law, Criminology and Police Sci., 59: 171-82, 1968.

12. Kaplan, J.: *Marijuana, The New Prohibition,* World Publishing Company, New York, 1970, p. 239.

13. Louria, D. B.: *The Drug Scene,* McGraw-Hill, New York, 1968, p. 108.

14. Miras, C., cited in Kaplan, J.: *Marijuana, The New Prohibition,* World Publishing Company, New York, 1970, p. 179.

15. Chopra, I. C., and Chopra, R. N.: United Nations Bulletin on Narcotics, 9: 23, 1957.

16. Benabud, A.: Int. J. Add., 3: 398, 1968.

17. Cannabis Report by the Advisory Committee on Drug Dependence, London, 1968, p. 7.

18. Smith, D. E.: J. Psychedelic Drugs, 2: 37, 1968.

19. Talbott, J. A., and Teague, J. W.: J. Amer. Med. Assoc. 210: 299, 1969.

20. Weil, A. T.: New Eng. J. Med. 282: 997, 1970.

21. Keeler, M. H., Reifler, C. B., and Liptzin, M. B.: Amer. J. Psychiat., 125: 384, 1968.

research progress

Most of the patients at the Phipps Clinic, the psychiatric division of the Johns Hopkins Hospital, are teen-agers. One aim of therapy is to help them feel that they are part of the "therapeutic community" of the ward, with responsibility for ward activities and authority to make decisions about ward rule together with the staff at community meetings. Within this program one method had been to encourage patients to take up a project to enhance the physical environment or functioning of the ward. Bob R. decided to beautify the ward by planting flowers and other greenery throughout the day-room. He lavished special attention on the cultivation of some of his plants. When asked about them, he would always reply, jokingly, "I'm growing myself some pot. It's cheaper than buying it." And the nurses and aides and doctors would laugh with him.

As the plants matured, Bob cut off the leaves and smaller branches and chopped them up: "To prepare the pot for smoking, Ha!" This had been going on for some weeks until a skeptical psychiatry resident went to the library, examined a botany text, returned to the ward and discovered that Bob had not been joking at all. He was indeed growing a marijuana plant, one with a heavy exudation of the psychoactive resin. After this incident I decided to learn a little botany, at least enough to identify the marijuana plant.

The Plant

The proper name for the marijuana plant is *Cannabis sativa,* and it is commonly known as hemp (see Chapter 1). It is a ubiquitous plant that grows successfully in a wide variety of climates and is used as a source of fiber as well as drugs. Plants that produce high concentrations of the mind-altering substances are the least valuable sources of fiber and *vice versa*; those that yield tough cord rarely can elicit a "high." It is difficult to determine why there is such a difference among strains of hemp. While most plants exist in wide variety of different taxonomic species, the genus, *Cannabis,* is generally regarded by botanists as having only one specie, *Cannabis sativa,* despite the existence of a number of variations of the plant.

The hemp plant is an annual, growing each year from seed. It is fairly easy to recognize, if one maintains a high index of suspicion. The plant has a rigid, herbaceous (grass-like as opposed to woody) stalk which varies in height from three to sixteen feet. The stalk is generally not round, but fluted or channeled with clearly defined nodes about a foot apart. When it is grown under spacious, uncrowded conditions, the hemp plant sprouts numerous branches and the stalk can become about two inches thick. If crowded, however, as it usually is when grown for fiber, the plant has very few branches or flowers except at the top, and the stems are only about an inch wide.

Hemp can be identified by the unique pattern of its leaves. They grow opposite to each other, in closely knit bundles containing about seven leaves, and fan out in symmetrical groups. The individual leaves are dark green, thin, and pointed at the end with small notches.

Hemp is supposed to be a dioecious plant, having two completely separate sexes. The males grow in small groups of about five stamens that discharge an abundance of yellow pollen. The pistillate or female flowers have a thin green flower cup, pointed with a slit at one side, which almost completely covers the ovary and barely permits two small stigmas (the structures which receive pollen) to protrude at their apex. The ovary contains just one seed, mottled gray or brown and only about a quarter-inch long. These are the seeds which can be used as bird food.

In 1923, however, a botanist discovered that hemp suffers from a rather confused sexual identity (1). He found that ordinary hemp has two distinct sexes if it is planted in the springtime. When grown in the greenhouse during the short light period of winter, however, about 90 per cent of the plants either reversed their sex or became hermaphroditic. He varied a number of factors, such as the temperature, in the greenhouse and the amount and duration of light shown on the plants, and concluded that the sex of the plant depended mainly on length of daylight period, and perhaps to a slight degree on richness of the soil.

According to another belief discussed in Chapter 1, only the female plants produce significant amounts of psychoactive resin. Evidence that the male plant contains the psychoactive resin was reported as early as 1908, when a team of pharmacists simply extracted male and female plants, injected extracts into animals and found that they were equally potent in disrupting animal behavior (2). But proponents of the female pre-eminence among cannabis plants argued rightly that one can hardly equate the capacity of a crude extract of the plant to make dogs stumble and fall with the intoxicating properties of marijuana in man.

In the 1960's delta-1-tetrahydrocannabinol (THC) was isolated, synthesized, and shown to be the primary psychoactive substance of marijuana. When methods were developed for measuring its concentration in hemp plants, it was shown that male and female plants have the same concentration of THC (3). Roots, large stalks, and seeds were found to contain very little THC. The smaller stems and leaves have moderate concentrations of THC, but the flowers and the pollen contain even more. Most of the THC is located in bracts (the leaves next to the flowers), where the concentration is about 11 per cent by weight. This is notable when contrasted to marijuana available in this country which usually contains less than 1 per cent THC.

It has long been known that marijuana grown in different parts of the world varies in potency. Marijuana from warmer climates, as in Mexico and India, is apparently much stronger than marijuana

Pistillate top with seed. *By Dewey in U.S.D.A. Yearbook.*

Staminate flowering top.   *By Dewey in U.S.D.A. Yearbook.*

from the mid-western United States. To test this commonly held be-lief, Doorenbos analyzed marijuana plants from different locales for their content of THC. Then he planted seeds of plants obtained from Mexico, Turkey, France, Italy, Sweden, Iowa, and Minnesota in a two-acre plantation near Oxford, Mississippi, sponsored by the U.S. government. Upon analyzing the newborn plants, he found that whether grown in Mexico or in Mississippi the Mexican plants pro-duced high concentrations of THC. Similarly, in the Minnesota plants the THC content was uniformly low whether they were grown in Minnesota or in Mississippi. Accordingly, Doorenbos con-cluded, "We have found that it is not where the plants are grown but where their parents come from that counts." (3).

The flowering tops of the male and female plants are covered by a multitude of glandular hairs. These give the appearance of many brilliant points, and if the tops are pressed between one's fingers a sticky and odorous resin is exuded. These glandular hairs are be-lieved to be the chief secretory organs for the THC-containing resin. When the secretion is sufficiently abundant, the cuticle of the gland breaks and the resin spreads over the surface of the leaves next to the flower. This accounts for Doorenbos's finding that these leaves, the bracts, have the highest content of THC.

Bouquet has suggested that the resin protects the plant against heat and dry weather (4). He offered this hypothesis after noticing that the resin is produced just at the time the seeds form and as the flowers are coming out. At these times they are most sensitive to dry heat and the resin would provide a sort of protective varnish. Bou-quet's hypothesis would explain why less resin is produced in cooler climates, where it would be less critical for the survival of the plant.

Measuring Marijuana in Plants and Animals

Chemists first began to investigate the active ingredients of the hemp plant in the 1840's, about the time that O'Shaughnessy introduced cannabis into European medicine. Among the early attempts to devise tests to identify the hemp extract, numerous color reactions were reported and one acquired general acceptance as a specific test for the psychoactive substance of cannabis. This was the "Beam Test," in which hemp extracts were mixed with a 5 per cent solution of potassium hydroxide in methanol. If a purple color developed the test was positive. Somehow this test survived for a hundred years as the *sine qua non* of marijuana chemistry. When Roger Adams and his group at the University of Illinois, in 1940, were able to purify a class of tetrahydrocannabinols which clearly reproduced in man the intoxicating properties of marijuana, they were surprised to find that their preparation proved negative on the Beam Test (5).

Before any progress toward the isolation of the active ingredients in marijuana could be made, it was necessary to have a relatively simple means of characterizing the psychotropic activity in animals. The one most commonly used was to assess the degree of inco-ordination in dogs. This rather crude measure was described in 1884 by the French physician Liataud (6). After the administration of marijuana, dogs first become quiet. Quite soon, however, they be begin to look somewhat apprehensive and to sway forward, backward, and side to side, an effect which becomes more pronounced with time. With large enough doses, they may fall over. To prevent this the dogs will often stand with their feet spread apart. Although they appear grossly inco-ordinated, the animals are able to perform fairly complicated movements and most of their reflexes remain normal.

In 1903, Fraenkel noticed that dogs in this state, when placed in abnormal positions, would make no effort to move (7). Their ability to maintain bizarre postures for prolonged periods resembled the catatonia exhibited by some schizophrenics, who at times may stand tilted over or extend one or more of their limbs for hours on end. Fraenkel concluded that marijuana was capable of producing an animal model of catatonia and hence might be considered a psychotomimetic drug.

The major problem with the dog ataxia (co-ordination) test was that the response of different dogs to the same dose of marijuana extract varied considerable. Only after the method was "cleaned up" and standard means of scoring the behavior of dogs applied did it succeed in providing reliable information about the relative potency of various marijuana preparations (8). Even then the test was far from perfect. In the process of isolating pure THC, Mechoulam's group also found a new derivative of marijuana called cannabichromene which appeared to be psychoactive since it was highly potent in producing inco-ordination in dogs (9). But when this substance was administered to humans, it produced no psychological effects at all, even in fairly large doses (10).

While the dog test did turn out to reflect the activity of THC, the same cannot be said of another well-known animal test for marijuana activity. Gayer found that cats, rabbits, and dogs developed anesthesia of the corneas of their eyes after intravenous injection of marijuana preparations dissolved in acetone (11). Since this anesthesia could be measured easily by tapping an animal's cornea with a delicate hair and noticing if the animal blinked his eyes, the Gayer test became a standard procedure for evaluating marijuana preparations. Many investigators used it despite the fact that it was beset by enormous inter-individual variations as well as great variations even in the same animal. To make matters even more confusing, results with the Gayer test did not always parallel the dog inco-ordination procedure, sometimes diverging as much as tenfold.

THC, The Chemical Breakthrough

With the technical advances that facilitated the isolation and synthesis of THC, it was soon possible to make a number of derivatives. Simply by adding an additional four carbons to the side chain of the THC molecule, the active dose of the material was lowered at least five times and the activity prolonged from a few hours to a few days (12). Another derivative also is several times more potent than THC and appears to have a different spectrum of effects (13). At low doses this derivative has no mind-altering actions but does cause a significant lowering of blood pressure and body temperature. It has been proposed as an agent in the treatment of high blood pressure and perhaps for hyperthermia associated with acute sunstroke.

In the recent acceleration of marijuana research, THC has been synthesized in radioactive form so that its fate in the bodies of animals and humans can be ascertained. In two years of research with radioactive THC, there have already been several surprises. When all tissues of the rabbit were examined for radioactive THC or products formed from it in the body, the brain turned out to be the tissue with the least radioactivity (14).

For those concerned about long-term dangers of marijuana, research with radioactive THC has provided fresh sources of alarm.

Δ′ THC

7-HYDROXY-Δ′ THC

THC or its breakdown products remain in the body long after the "high" is over. One week after injecting rats with radioactive THC, researchers found the radioactivity at more than half its original level within the animal's body tissues (14).

A resolution of the paradox that experienced users of marijuana, instead of becoming tolerant to its effects, actually appear to be more sensitive than neophytes may emerge from other experiments dealing with the metabolism of radioactive THC in man and animals. The first known metabolite (breakdown product) of THC was recently identified in rats and rabbits (12, 15). It is formed by the addition of a hydroxyl group (oxygen plus hydrogen) to a carbon attached to one of the rings (the terpene one) of THC.*

This metabolite appears to possess considerable psychoactivity in mice and monkeys, though it has yet to be given to man. In fact, when injected directly into the brains of mice it is fifteen times more potent in disrupting behavior than THC itself (27). It is formed by

* This compound, 11-hydroxy-trans-delta-8-tetrahydrocannabinol or 7-hydroxy-trans-delta-1-tetrahydrocannabinol (with the pyran and substituted monoterpene numbering systems respectively), was first identified as a metabolite of the delta-1(6)-THC (monoterpene numbering), which is only present to a limited extent in marijuana extracts. Delta-1(6)-THC is equal in apparent psychotropic potency in animals to the major psychoactive component delta-1-THC from which it may be formed on smoking. More recently the identical metabolite has been shown to arise from delta-1-THC (16).

enzyme systems in the liver which normally metabolize drugs. These drug-metabolizing enzymes are well known to be "inducible"; that is, on repeated exposure to a drug, the enzymes become progressively more active in degrading it. If the mental effects of marijuana are caused not by THC itself, but by the "active" hydroxylated metabolite formed in the liver, one could easily explain the "sensitization" of experienced users. With each succeeding drug experience, the livers of the marijuana smokers would become increasingly efficient at forming the psychoactive metabolite. Mechoulam (12) cites as evidence in favor of this hypothesis the finding that THC elicits more behavioral effects in animals when injected intraperitoneally (into the abdominal cavity) than when injected subcutaneously. When a drug is injected intraperitoneally, it proceeds directly to the liver and is much more likely to be acted on by drug-metabolizing enzymes there than when it is administered subcutaneously.

Another study using radioactive THC carried out at the National Institute of Mental Health by Louis Lemberger and colleagues, including Julius Axelrod, who won the 1970 Nobel Prize in Medicine and Physiology, may support Mechoulam's hypothesis (17). Injecting radioactive THC into humans, this group found that in subjects who had never smoked marijuana the half-life (time for levels to fall by 50 per cent) of THC in the blood was 56 hours. With experienced users, who maintained that they had smoked marijuana every day for the past year, THC disappeared twice as fast from the blood. This was, at first, perplexing since it suggested that experienced users were exposed to less THC than novices, and hence should be less rather than more affected by the drug. But if marijuana's psychoactivity in man is associated primarily with a THC metabolite, then this finding would be consistent with the hypothesis that the "sensitization" of experienced users results from enhanced metabolism of THC in the liver.

Animal Models of Human Behavior

Just as the attempts of pharmacologists to develop a behavioral bioassay of marijuana have been halting and ineffectual, so their attempts to explain human behavior on the basis of the drug's effects in mice or rats have not been terribly enlightening. It remains uncertain that the apparent behavioral effects of marijuana in small animals bear any relationship to psychotropic actions in man, yet there have been suggestive findings. Loewe attempted thirty years ago to explain why cannabis helps people to sleep (18). After finding that marijuana extracts did not directly put animals to sleep, he tried to determine if they would prolong sleep induced in mice by barbiturates. And indeed animals slept longer when treated with marijuana in conjunction with barbiturates than when receiving barbiturates alone. Yet cannabinol, one of the constituents of marijuana which is devoid of marijuana-like activity in man, showed the highest potency of all the components of marijuana in this test. And paradoxically, while marijuana helped barbiturates put mice to sleep, it also potentiated the ability of amphetamine to excite them (19).

When Carlini and Kramer injected rats with an extract of cannabis, the animals became excited and soon showed signs of increased spontaneous activity (20). Their appetite also seemed to be enhanced, although this may merely have been related to the fact that they were moving around more and so encountered the food tray more often, much like hyperexcitable, nervous people who pace the floor of their houses and find themselves constantly opening the refrigerator for a snack. At the time of maximum locomotor activity, about 30 minutes after injecting the drug, rats tended to fight with each other. Later they became lethargic and would not look for food at all. At this point the rats seemed to be hypersensitive, since they would make chirping noises whenever touched. Soon thereafter, the investigators observed a "catatonic stupor" in the rats. Although wide awake, the animals remained in a fixed position without moving, even when the cage was shaken. After about 12 hours they appeared completely normal.

Remarkably, despite the array of behavioral aberrations just described, rats receiving marijuana extracts performed at least as well in running mazes as did control animals. Even more surprisingly, after several trials they performed significantly better than the control group.

A group of investigators headed by Daniel X. Freedman, a leading psychopharmacologist at the University of Chicago, recently was able to reproduce with THC the behavioral effects of marijuana in mice (21). With what seemed to be moderate doses of THC for mice, the animals' motor behavior showed the same sort of inco-ordination as Fraenkel's dogs, which had been injected with crude marijuana extracts. Moreover, the mice were hyperreactive to sound and touch, just as human marijuana smokers are. Despite this hypersensitivity to sensory stimuli, they displayed a decrease in spontaneous activity.

There may be an animal model for the psychotomimetic effect of THC considerably more meaningful than mice. Some investigators have found that in monkeys, THC elicits behavioral changes very much like those of LSD (22). Monkeys became stimulated or depressed depending on the dose of THC. Moreover, they appeared to be hallucinating and lost either the ability or motivation to perform complex tasks.

THC and LSD

LSD and other psychedelic drugs produce characteristic neurochemical changes in animal brains. They alter the concentrations of two neurotransmitters (chemicals which transmit nerve impulses), norepinephrine and serotonin, which are thought to be involved in the regulation of emotional behavior. LSD produces a rise in brain serotonin and a fall in brain norepinephrine, and the time course of these changes is correlated with the behavioral effects of the drug. THC has produced similar effects in the concentrations of these substances in mouse brain, although the alteration in serotonin metabolism was not exactly the same as with LSD. (21)

The work with the most direct bearing in human subjects on the relationship of marijuana to the psychedelic drugs has been done by Harris Isbell, well known for his pioneering studies in assessing the psychotropic potency of a large series of LSD analogues. Isbell administered progressively increasing doses of THC to ex-heroin addicts who were familiar with marijuana. At low doses they were unable to distinguish the effects of marijuana from those of THC. Subjects became euphoric, felt time was slowing down, and felt their perceptions to be keener. When the dose of THC was increased fivefold, however, marked distortions in visual and auditory perception emerged. Subjects felt disembodied and unreal, and experienced hallucinations.

These experiences resembled those produced by LSD but were not identical. The subjects were also given LSD on a different occasion. Their subjective experiences with the two drugs were readily distinguished by a "subjective effects" questionnaire. Still, these findings provide substantiation for the assumption that the marijuana usually smoked in the United States produces mild, pleasant effects largely because it contains very little THC.

Leo Hollister performed experiments similar to Isbell's, and with high doses he also found that THC is very much like LSD (23). But whereas people taking LSD are extremely alert throughout the drug experience, with THC Hollister's subjects became sleepy—more and more so as time passed. In fact, coming down from their "high," they would spend most of their time sleeping, despite which they also slept soundly the night following the trials.

Hollister's subjects reported frequent bursts of disconnected dreaming during their several hours of drug-induced sleep, and this finding could be of considerable practical importance. Most sleeping medicines suppress dreaming, a side effect which many sleep researchers feel might account for their habituating and addicting potential. It is possible that some THC derivative would serve as a sedative drug which enhances rather than diminishes dreaming and which therefore might be safer for medical use.

Another way in which the two drugs differed in Hollister's experiment was in the prominence and persistance of euphoria with THC. Subjects were happy throughout the course of the experiment. With LSD, while some giggling and uncontrollable laughter was frequently encountered for very brief periods at first, subjects soon were beset with either awe or fear.

Perhaps the reason why THC does not produce LSD's overwhelming effects is related to the fact that it will not stimulate the sympathetic nervous system, as LSD does throughout the body. The sympathetic nervous system regulates fight-and-flight types of effects such as the increase in blood sugar and in blood levels of fatty acids, chemicals which are a major source of energy. THC lowers blood pressure and has no effect on blood sugar or fatty acids. The only consistent outward physical changes that Hollister and Isbell observed were an increase in pulse rate and reddening of the conjunctivae (the pink membranes that line the eyes).

Tolerance, Withdrawal, Addiction?

In any discussion of drugs which may be subject to abuse, the words "tolerance," "withdrawal," and "addiction" often crop up. What these words mean in precise scientific terms has been a task to which pharmacologists have addressed themselves for years, but they may be given simple operational definitions. Tolerance is the need for progressively larger doses of a drug in order to produce a given effect as the drug is taken more and more frequently. This is a well-known phenomenon with opiates, alcohol, barbiturates, and the amphetamines. Tolerance to LSD and other psychedelic drugs also develops, but this is quite short-lived.

Withdrawal refers to the severe physical reaction that occurs when a human or animal who has been regularly taking large doses of a drug to which he has developed tolerance, abruptly stops using the drug. Symptoms of withdrawal from heroin include trembling, nausea, vomiting, goose flesh, dilation of the pupils, tearing, runny nose, yawning, and sneezing. With severe withdrawal there is elevation of body temperature and blood pressure. Despite the severe symptoms of heroin withdrawal, few deaths occur.

Withdrawal from alcohol or barbiturates, on the other hand, can prove fatal. Symptoms range from gross tremors, disorientation, and hallucinations to convulsions and respiratory arrest. Few people appreciate the fact that the minor tranquilizers such as meprobamate (Miltown or Equanil), as well as several sleeping medications such as glutethimide (Doriden), can be similarly addicting. Withdrawal from all of these sedative drugs is very similar and resembles the well-known picture of alcoholic withdrawal called delirium tremens, the "DT's." Since these drugs seem to be interrelated in their pharmacological actions, withdrawal from any one of them can be treated by administering one of the others. Thus, addicts to meprobamate are usually treated with gradually reduced doses of barbiturates.

According to some definitions of addiction, the existence of well-defined tolerance and withdrawal are the sufficient and necessary criteria. However, many authorities feel that another more crucial feature is essential for addiction, namely a "craving" for the drug. The lives of heroin addicts are not destroyed just because they are tolerant to opiates and will undergo withdrawal symptoms when they stop taking them. Addicts do not keep taking heroin merely to escape withdrawal symptoms. Even afer being completely withdrawn from heroin for several months, and thus having no apparent "physical" need for the drug, addicts will return to their habit. This may well have a sociological explanation. The drug addict may feel ill at ease with "straight" people and gravitate back to the same social contacts, including the narcotic pushers, as before. It is still possible, however, that particular cells in addicts' brains develop a "thirst" for opium.

Animals can clearly be shown to develop craving or at least a preference for many drugs. Experimentally, they are equipped with catheters and devices for injecting themselves intravenously with a test drug or some control solution. Animals will self-administer opiates with great avidity. They will also inject themselves with amphetamines. It is more difficult, although possible, to demonstrate a preference in animals for alcohol.

Thus, addiction seems to involve at least three processes: tolerance, withdrawal, and "craving," which may be the most important component though it is poorly defined. How does this apply to cannabis? In human studies chronic marijuana smokers do not show much evidence of tolerance (24). If anything, they develop a greater sensitivity to the psychological effects of the drug after prolonged use. Whether this is true "inverse" tolerance or whether it reflects the ability of experienced marijuana users to inhale the drug more efficiently or to perceive subtle nuances of drug effects at low doses remains unclear.

There has, however, been a general impression among those who are acquainted with chronic marijuana users, that they may well become tolerant to the effects of the drug. Some experimental evidence for this view has been obtained in studies in which extremely heavy marijuana users appeared to be less sensitive than one might expect to fairly high doses of marijuana taken by mouth. (25, 28)

There is some direct evidence that tolerance to THC does develop, at least in pigeons. Pigeons are excellent subjects for conditioning studies since they can be trained to peck at a key for food under extremely intricate schedules. A dose of THC was found which, while not so large as to be toxic, sufficed to completely suppress all pecking (26). After five days at the same dose of THC, the birds' rate of responding returned to normal levels. Then the investigators gradually increased the dose of THC, ultimately to levels twenty times the original dose. On the twenty-seventh day of THC administration, a dose twenty times that which originally had completely suppressed pecking no longer did so. At this stage THC was stopped abruptly. No gross behavioral symptoms were observed, nor did the general health of the pigeons seem to be impaired. The marked degree of tolerance and the time course over which it developed resembled what the same investigators observed in pigeons receiving morphine. Other addictive drugs, such as barbiturates, never produce nearly that much tolerance. Of course, in these experiments THC differed from morphine in one extremely important feature. THC tolerance was not associated with any observable withdrawal symptoms.

The principles of tolerance and "cross-tolerance" can help to determine whether marijuana and psychedelic drugs act in the same way or at the same sites in the brain. Tolerance is well known to develop to the effects of LSD, although it is short-lived and is not associated with any withdrawal symptoms. Thus, a given dose of LSD taken tomorrow will not produce as intense a reaction as did the same dose taken today. However, less than a week from today LSD will again display its original potency. Over the years, Harris Isbell has compared a number of psychedelic drugs in terms of tolerance and cross-tolerance. If cross-tolerance were to exist between LSD and mescaline, a given dose of LSD today should attenuate the effects of mescaline given tomorrow. This is indeed what happens with psychedelic drugs in human subjects. Cross-tolerance exists among all the psychedelic drugs including LSD, mescaline, and psilocybin. But no cross-tolerance can be shown between LSD and drugs which are not psychedelic, such as amphetamines. One can then conclude that LSD and the other psychedelic drugs probably act in a similar way at the same or similar sites in the brain.

In his experiments at the Lexington Narcotics Hospital, Isbell gave ex-heroin addicts LSD injections at increasing doses every day for ten days. On the eleventh day all the subjects were fully tolerant to LSD. But on the twelfth day they still responded to THC as they had two weeks earlier. These results indicate that marijuana and LSD act in different ways at different places in the brain. (29)

Future Possibilities

Chemists and pharmacologists should, within a short time, learn the fate of THC in the bodies of animals and man. Already, one major breakdown product, which appears to be psychoactive and might mediate the behavioral actions of marijuana, is known. Others will probably be discovered. The rate at which they are formed in and excreted from the body will be determined. How steady marijuana smokers and non-users metabolize THC can then be studied, and valuable information explaining the physical acculturation of users to the drug should emerge.

Large numbers of new chemical analogues of THC will probably be synthesized and evaluated in animals and man. Some are likely to elicit the varying aspects of marijuana intoxication to differing degrees. Some may have sedative effects but not make the user "high." Such derivatives might be ideal sleeping medications since even with massive overdoses they could not be used for suicide. Moreover, such drugs would probably not be as habit forming as most current sleeping pills. One THC derivative presently known seems to be considerably more potent in lowering blood pressure than in "stoning" people. It may spawn a collection of new antihypertensive medications.

As more and more investigators administer marijuana or THC to humans and animals for extensive periods, toxic effects may emerge. Since cannabis has been in use for thousands of years, it is unlikely that any gross physical abnormalities will turn out to result from marijuana use, but there may be some surprises. Fifty years ago, no one would have suspected tobacco, smoked since time immemorial, as a major cause of heart attacks, respiratory disease, and lung cancer.

Finally, questions about how marijuana exerts its effects on the brain may be answered. What neuronal systems are altered to produce its effects which resemble both psychedelic drugs and alcohol? Are the biogenic amines, which appear to be neurotransmitters in emotional areas of the brain, to be implicated? These interesting chemicals seem to be involved in the actions of almost all known psychoactive drugs. But in this area progress is likely to be slow. The secrets of how drugs act have always been notoriously resistant to the probings of curious researchers. Aspirin, for instance, has been studied extensively for almost a century, and still we do not know how it relieves headaches.

References

1. Schaffner, J. H.: Ecology, 4:323, 1923.
2. Houghton, E. M., and Hamilton, H. C.: Amer. J. Pharm., 80:16, 1908.
3. Doorenbos, N.: Ann. N. Y. Acad. Sci., 1971, in press.
4. Bouquet, J.: Arch. Inst. Pastor, 26:288, 1937.
5. Adams, R.: Bull. N. Y. Acad. Med., 18:705, 1942.
6. Liataud, A.: Compt, Rend. Acad. Sci., 18:149, 1844.
7. Fraenkel, S.: Arch. F. Exptl. Rath. U. Pharm., file 49, page 266, 1903.
8. Loewe, S.: J. Pharm. Exptl. Ther., 66:23, 1939.
9. Gaoni, Y., and Mechoulam, R.: Chem. Comm., 1:20, 1966.
10. Isbell, H., Gorodetzky, C. W., Jasinski, D., Claussen, U., Von Spulak, F., and Korte, F.: Psychopharmacologia, 11:184, 1967.
11. Gayer, H.: Arch. F. Exptl. Path. U., Pharm., 129:312, 1928.
12. Mechoulam, R.: Science, 168:1159, 1970.
13. Sim, V.: in *Psychotomimetic Drugs,* edited by Daniel H. Efron, Raven Press, New York, 1970, p. 333.
14. Agurell, S., Nilsson, I. M., Ohlsson, A., and Sandberg, F.: Biochem. Pharmacol., 18:1195, 1969.
15. Foltz, R. L., Fentiman, A. F., Jr., Leighty, E. G., Walter, J. L., Drewes, H. R., Schwartz, W. E., Page, T. F., Jr., and Truitt, E. B., Jr.: Science, 168:844, 1970.
16. Wall, M. E., Brine, D. R., Brine, G. A., Pitt, C. G., Freudenthal, R. I., and Christensen, H. D.: J. Am. Chem. Soc., 92:3446, 1970.
17. Lemberger, L., Silberstein, S. D., Axelrod, J., and Kopin, I. J.: Science, 170:1320-1322, 1970.
18. Loewe, S.: J. Amer. Pharmaceutical Assoc., 29:162, 1940.
19. Loewe, S.: Arch. Exptl. Path. Pharmacol., 211:175, 1950..
20. Carlini, E. A., and Kramer, C.: Psychopharmacologia, 7:175, 1965.
21. Holtzman, D., Lovell, R. A., Jaffe, J. H., and Freedman, D. X.: Science, 163:1464, 1969.
22. Scheckel, C. L., Boff, E., Dahlen, P., and Smart, T.: Science, 160:1467, 168.
23. Hollister, L. E., Richers, R. K., and Gillespie, H. K.: Clin. Pharmacol. Thera., 9:783, 1968.

24. Weil, A. T., Zinberg, N. E., and Nelsen, J. M.: Science, 162:1234, 1969.
25. Jones, R. T., and Stone, G. C.: Psychopharmacologia, 18:108, 1970.
26. McMillan, D., Harris, L. S., Frankenheim, J. M., and Kennedy, J. S.: Science, 169:501, 1970.
27. Christensen, H. D., Freudenthal, R. I., Boegli, G., Testino, L., Brine, D. R., Pitt, C. G., Wall, M. E.: Science, 172:165, 1971.
28. Jones, R.: Fed. Proc. 1971, in press.
29. Isbell, H., and Jasinski, D. R.: Psychopharmacologia, 14:115, 1969.

legal turmoil

It is an understatement to say that the legal status of marijuana in the United States represents a pressing and difficult problem. Current laws regulating marijuana are quite varied and for the most part highly inappropriate. Classification and punishment of offenses involving marijuana, LSD, morphine, and cocaine are usually treated in the same manner, even though the effects of the drugs and their patterns of use are very different. Until quite recently Massachusetts law provided that anyone present in a house where marijuana is kept or who is in the company of a person in possession of any amount of marijuana may be "arrested without a warrant, and may be punished by imprisonment in the state prison for not more than five years" (1). In most states in early 1971, simple possession of marijuana is a felony while in others the offense has been reduced to misdemeanor status. In Nebraska, for instance, the maximum penalty for simple possession as a first offense is seven days, yet in Texas the same offense carries a minimum sentence of two years and a maximum of life imprisonment.

Penalties for sale are even more draconian. Next to first-degree

Eugene Anthony.

murder, the sale of marijuana is the most harshly punished crime in Rhode Island—penalties are more severe than for second-degree murder, armed robbery, and rape. Conviction for the sale of marijuana to anyone under age twenty-one brings with it a sentence of thirty years to life imprisonment. But Rhode Island is lenient when compared with Georgia and Colorado, where sale of marijuana to a minor can result in the death penalty.

Such harshly and irrational legislation exists for several reasons. In 1932 a Uniform Narcotics Drug Act was designed to offer each state a comprehensive ready-made plan for possible adoption. At that time marijuana was little known throughout the country except through yellow journalism, and its use was confined to the lower socio-economic strata in certain southern states. Sensational newspaper reports in the late 1920's spreading the myth of marijuana as a "killer drug" and widespread ignorance of the actual properties of the drug facilitated the lumping together of the opiates and marijuana under the Uniform Narcotics Drug Act. In the next decade a national information campaign, again labeling marijuana as an extremely dangerous drug capable of destroying minds and provoking acts of violence, was launched for passage of the 1937 Marijuana Tax Act.

The Marijuana Tax Act was designed to ban marijuana indirectly through a revenue system. An excise tax of $100 per ounce was levied on the transfer of marijuana. Of course, since all states had criminal penalties for the possession and sale of the drug, anyone offering to pay the tax was liable for prosecution under state law. After a number of amendments over the years (until May 1971 when it was superseded by new legislation), the federal law declared possession of marijuana a felony punishable by two to ten years imprisonment while sale of the drug could bring a sentence of five to twenty years. More realistic than many state laws, federal legislation distinguished between the "hard drugs" (opiates) and marijuana, with milder penalties for marijuana.

In the 1960's the extensive use of marijuana by middle-class students and young adults and the beginnings of rigorous scientific research prompted a greater awareness of the true nature of the effects of marijuana on people. Finally, on October 14, 1970, the two Houses of the United States Congress passed a new law, H. R. 18583,

Eugene Anthony.

London Daily Express.

known as the "Comprehensive Drug Abuse Prevention and Control Act of 1970." Whatever its influence on state laws will be, H. R. 18583 classifies possession of marijuana as a misdemeanor punishable by no more than one year in jail while it raises penalties for professional drug pushers over what they were under the earlier federal law. Sensibly, an amendment provides that if a person gives away a small amount of marijuana and receives no money for it, he is treated as a possessor rather than a vendor of the drug. Moreover, under the new law judges have the discretion to deem the first offense for possession of marijuana non-criminal. As a reflection of the growing interest in obtaining scientific data on marijuana, the law provides for a "Commission on Marijuana and Drug Abuse" with a budget of up to one million dollars to prepare a comprehensive report on the drug.

The trend toward increasing leniency in dealing with marijuana users appears to be accelerating in some states even more than in the federal law. In the Maryland State House of Delegates on February 2, 1971, delegates King and Lombardi introduced a bill which would remove any prison sentence for possession of marijuana and, for a first offense, would provide a maximum fine of $250 (Maryland House of Delegates Bill 263, 1971). This bill would not treat marijuana possession much differently from a traffic violation.

An even bolder approach is being advocated in the New York State Assembly, where delegate Franz Leichter, representing the Manhattan district encompassing Columbia University, introduced a bill that would legalize the use and sale of marijuana almost as if it were an alcoholic beverage, with some features resembling current regulations of cigarette advertising. Among its provisions are the following:

> There shall be established a marijuana control authority which shall license and regulate growers, producers, manufacturers and distributors of marijuana. . . . The authority shall prescribe the strength of marijuana to be sold at retail . . . and shall also prescribe a suitable warning on every package of marijuana regarding possible ill effects on the health of the user. . . . Marijuana may be sold at retail *only* in licensed liquor stores. . . . There are no restrictions on the amount of marijuana a person may buy. It shall how-

ever be unlawful to sell (and give) any marijuana to a person under eighteen years of age. . . . All marijuana will be taxed in an amount similar to cigarettes. [F. S. Leichter, personal communication].

Proponents of Leichter's bill did not anticipate passage in 1971 but felt confident that this or similar legislation would be enacted within two to four years. Even the proposal of such legislation seems to indicate a great change of public opinion or the upsurge of attitudes held by a new generation.

The question of the optimal legal status of marijuana is now frequently posed by young and old. John Kaplan, a professor of law at Stanford, has devoted an exhaustive and eloquent volume to this question and has provided extensive background information to justify

World Wide Photos.

his arguments (2). His book is called *Marijuana: The New Prohibition* because he feels that the present role of marijuana in American society is quite analogous to that of alcohol during the prohibition era. And for marijuana he favors a "repeal of prohibition."

Kaplan argues that in formulating laws to regulate a psychotropic substance we try to balance the benefits versus the costs to society. Thus, while alcohol consumption was considered a vice and while prohibition perhaps reduced the incidence of severe alcoholism, the cost of prohibition to society was excessive and its repeal was a wise decision. These intolerable costs included the massive expense of attempting to enforce a law which a large segment of the population often broke and the physical ill effects such as blindness caused by drinking black-market wood alcohol. More important, Kaplan stresses the harm to national morale when so large a portion of the population flaunts the law and thus becomes "criminal."

All of these considerations, Kaplan maintains, can be applied to the current marijuana problem. Forcing marijuana users to employ black-market preparations means they are more likely to become involved with "hard drugs" such as heroin. The preparations available vary greatly in strength. And in the case of marijuana, a large number of the people who become criminalized are young and impressionable.

Among the alternative approaches to the regulation of marijuana that Kaplan discusses is a "vice" model similar to that applied to prositution and gambling. Using this model, one would punish the seller but not the buyer. But this would still leave the supply of marijuana in a "black market," making it impossible for society to control the quality of the drug. And it is unlikely that the vice model would have its intended effect of markedly reducing or abolishing the use of marijuana.

The model favored by Kaplan is the licensing of the sale of alcoholic beverages. Thus, Kaplan favors legalizing marijuana with an age limit of sixteen. This would allow society to control the standards of purity and potency, and it could eliminate the underground market, helping prevent the graduation to drugs more harmful than marijuana. Of course, legalization might, on the other hand, greatly increase the number of marijuana users.

Before deciding on the optimal legal solution to the marijuana problem, a pivotal question must be answered. Assuming that moderate use of the drug is safe, should the law nonetheless "deprive the majority of moderate and safe users of their drug in order to protect the few abusers from their folly?" To a certain extent the answer depends on the numerical balance between the few abusers and the many who will use the drug moderately.

But to talk merely of numbers and of medical safety, of course, is an oversimplification. The nation is divided by sharply differing life styles and views of many social issues. Marijuana is symbolic of a more passive, contemplative, and less competitive attitude toward life than has been traditional in the United States. It is usually denounced by people who like things the way they are. Whether society accepts or rejects the drug will undoubtedly have some influence on the evolution of our national character.

References

1. Massachusetts General Laws Annotated, Chapter 94, s213A, 1966 supplement.
2. Kaplan, J.: *Marijuana: The New Prohibition,* World Publishing Company, New York, 1970.

index